Eating for

Sustained Energy 1

Eating for Sustained Energy 1

Liesbet Delport RD(SA) and Gabi Steenkamp RD(SA)

Dedication

To all those with diabetes, who for so long have had to eat 'special' foods containing no sugar, and often tasting like cardboard. Because of the Glycemic Index, they can now enjoy normal, lower fat, lower GI foods that are best for everyone who wishes to enjoy sustained energy.

Acknowledgements

We wish to thank Jan Delport, who managed this project originally. Without his input, the book would not be what it is today.

A great big thank you to our families for their patience and support while we prepared and tried out all these dishes, until they were perfect. Thank you to Neville and Wilma for the excellent photography of the dishes in the book, as well as the styling.

To all our colleagues for their support and for their enthusiastic use of all our books among their patients.
Last but not least our thanks to the publishers, Dick Wilkins, Anita Pyke and Ansie Kamffer and the editors, Elize Lubbe and Pat Barton, for their faith in this project.
We also humbly acknowledge the hand of the Lord in getting this book to fruition.

First edition, first impression 2006
Fourth impression 2008

Tafelberg
An imprint of NB Publishers
40 Heerengracht, Cape Town, 8000

ISBN: 0-624-04434-3
ISBN: 978-0-624-04434-5

EDITORS	Elize Lubbe and Pat Barton
PROOFREADERS	Estelle Crowson and Roxanne Reid
PHOTOGRAPHY	Neville Lockhart
FOOD STYLIST	Wilma Howells
DESIGN AND TYPESETTING	Lindie Metz and Valerie Phipps-Smith
REPRODUCTION	Virtual Colour cc., Cape Town
PRINTING	Printed and bound in China by WKT Company Limited

Contents

Authors' foreword

When we originally compiled *Eating for Sustained Energy 1*, we had seven aims: we wanted each recipe to be really tasty, quick and easy to make, using ingredients that are affordable and readily available in any home, while also being lower in fat and having lower Glycemic Index (GI) values than regular recipes. Our readers assure us just about every day that we have reached each and every one of these aims. In fact, we have had so many requests from satisfied readers for more recipes that we decided to compile *Eating for Sustained Energy 2.* It is now time to revamp *Eating for Sustained Energy 1*, as nutritional knowledge has moved on since we compiled this book six years ago. This revamped version has all the new Glycemic Load (GL) information added, as well as the latest GI values of foods tested over the last six years. It is our hope that you will enjoy the new look and feel of the book, which still contains the original tried and tested recipes. Each recipe has a brand-new photograph, so that you can see clearly, in a more up-to-date style, what you are going to make and how the end product is going to look. Some of our readers tell us that it is just as well that we have a photograph for each recipe, because if they had simply judged by the ingredients, they would have thought that everything would turn out to be muesli, especially in the baking section!

When we started writing *Eating for Sustained Energy*, we had no publisher and no idea that these kinds of recipes were going to be so popular. What we had was a lot of enthusiasm and the knowledge that it is not that difficult to compile tasty, healthy recipes. In fact, we were both cooking and baking such dishes for our families every day! It had to be shared with you, the public. Now, after 80 000+ copies of *Eating for Sustained Energy 1* have been sold in the six years it has been on the market, with sales that are still increasing, we know that these recipes work!

Used regularly, they help to lower diabetic individuals' blood glucose levels from over 20 mmol/l to below 10mmol/l, and to reduce cholesterol levels, blood pressure, hyperinsulinaemia and insulin resistance, as well as alleviate the symptoms of chronic candida, polycystic ovarian syndrome and inflammatory diseases such as arthritis. They also help children who suffer from Attention Deficit (Hyperactivity) Disorder to concentrate, overweight people to lose weight more easily, fatigued people to have more energy and sportsmen to perform better.

In this revamped version, we have included a new value in the nutritional box, i.e. the GL. This is explained in detailed, yet easy-to-understand, terms in the introduction. Unlike the GI, you can add up the GL values of all your meals and snacks and get your total GL per day! We have also condensed and updated the introduction for easier reading.

Our handy South African Glycemic Index and Load has also been of great help to many. It helps you to identify, quickly and easily, the GI and GL of most carbohydrate-rich foods eaten in South Africa, as it includes a cross-referenced alphabetical list of foods. It also contains the fat, fibre, protein, carbohydrate and kJ content per typical portion of food. Many people like to keep the GI and GL Guide with them when they shop, so that they can quickly check the GI of any food.

Our book on weight management, *Eat Smart and Stay Slim: the GI Diet*, is rapidly carving a niche for itself amongst all the slimming books. People say that it helps their mind to think right about getting thin and staying thin. The book is so packed with information that they want to read it over and over until they have absorbed everything. It also makes such compelling reading, that they can't put it down once they have started reading it. The weight management book contains a few recipes at the back, as well as a handy section containing meals for a week, on which you can lose weight by combining any breakfast, lunch, dinner and two to three snacks per day. Other invaluable information on how to get off the treadmill of compulsive eating, label-reading skills, fat-proofing your meals, as well as motivation to start exercising is also included. Our recipe books *Eating For Sustained Energy 1* and *Eating For Sustained Energy 2* supply you with many more delicious recipes to help with weight management, blood glucose control, general healthy eating and improved sport performance.

May you enjoy this book as much as all our others!

Liesbet and Gabi

Foreword

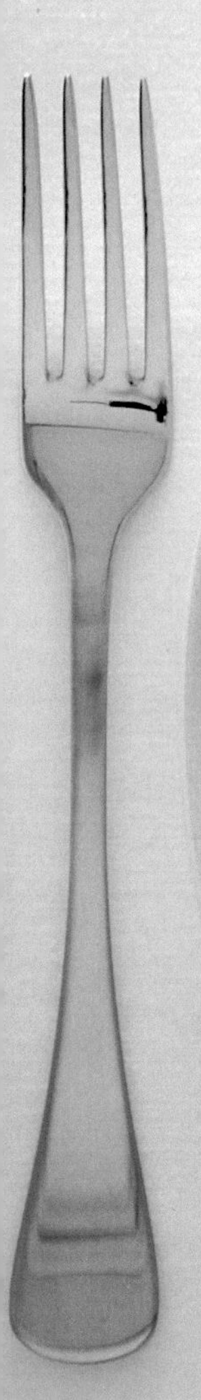

For many years people with diabetes have been traumatised, first of all by their diagnosis, but even more so by the traditional diabetic dietary guidelines that are prescribed as a result, particularly the 'no sugar' requirement. People with diabetes often suffer from a guilty conscience when breaking their prescribed diet. They become 'prisoners of a diet' which, under the best of circumstances, is difficult to follow and requires a great deal of sacrifice.

Over the past two decades scientists have begun to understand more about the physiological effect of different carbohydrates. The amount and type of carbohydrates are not absolute determinants of blood sugar levels. What really matters is the rate of digestion and absorption of carbohydrates. Therefore in any attempt to stabilise fluctuating blood sugar levels, the critical element will be the use of a tool that reflects the body's response to the carbohydrate food, as well as a thorough understanding of all the factors that may have an influence, whether they be negative or positive.

The Glycemic Index (GI) of foods has proven to be an accurate and successful tool in educating people about achieving and maintaining a stable blood sugar level. Although the Glycemic Index is easy to use in making better food choices, most people are still at a loss when it comes to implementing the recommended dietary guidelines into their daily routine. Using this recipe book removes the effort. In addition, the valuable tips and extra information provided for each recipe add extra value to the publication, making it even more useful and practical for all health-conscious people.

The added information regarding the fat, fibre, protein and sodium content of foods broadens the usefulness, not only to people with diabetes, but also to those suffering from coronary heart disease and hypoglycaemia, as well as to sportspersons and slimmers.

Conditions for claims regarding the Glycemic Index value of carbohydrate-rich foods have been included in the Proposed New Draft Food Labelling Regulations. Consumers can therefore be assured that the GI concept is reliable, and that it is a very practical way of ensuring effective blood sugar control.

Antoinette Booyzen
Registered Dietician of the Department of Health,
Directorate Food Control.

Introduction

Most people feel they could do with more sustained energy.

'I'm always tired!'

'I have no energy!'

We hear this every day in our modern stressed world where chronic fatigue is the norm.

We believe that the solution lies in eating correctly. By learning how to use the Glycemic Index (GI) and consuming a lower fat diet, one can attain an endless supply of energy. Resorting to all sorts of 'pick-me-up-quick' tonics or caffeine, or alcohol and cigarettes to relax, will no longer be necessary. Carbohydrate (CHO) is the body's source of fuel and, if you consume the right type at the proper time, you should have sustained energy, instead of feeling hyped up one moment and hitting the depths the next. Eating the lower fat way and following the GI will regulate blood glucose levels, keeping them stable, and result in your feeling great all the time.

In the past, it was assumed that complex CHO or starches, such as potatoes, mealiemeal and bread, were digested and absorbed slowly, resulting in only a slight rise in blood glucose levels. Simple sugars, on the other hand, were believed to be digested and absorbed quickly, producing a large and rapid rise in blood glucose levels. We now know that these assumptions were incorrect, and that the general public, as well as those with diabetes, no longer need to avoid sugar altogether, provided they use it correctly. In fact, we now know that table sugar has a slightly more favourable effect on the blood glucose of normal and diabetic individuals than do potatoes, bread and a few other starches, if used on their own.

As early as the 1930s scientists challenged the assumption that 'all CHO(s) were created equal' and that the metabolic effects of CHO can be predicted by classifying them as either 'simple' or 'complex'. In the 1970s researchers such as Otto and Crapo examined the glycemic impact of a range of foods containing CHO. To standardise the interpretation of glycemic response (the effect of food on blood glucose levels) data, Jenkins and colleagues of the University of Toronto, Canada, proposed the GI in 1981.

The Glycemic Index is a blood glucose indicator, where gly = glucose, emic = blood and index = an indicator. This work of Jenkins disproved the assumption that equivalent amounts of CHO from different foods cause similar glycemic responses. Furthermore, the researchers concluded that the CHO exchange lists that have regulated the diets of most people with diabetes do not reflect the physiological effect of foods and are therefore no longer sufficient to control blood glucose levels.

Scientists have proved, with research done over the past three decades, that it is not so much the **amount** of CHO, but rather **its rate of digestion and absorption into the blood stream** that determines the physiological response of the body. Research conducted all over the world since then confirms that the new way of rating foods according to their actual effect on blood glucose is scientifically more correct.

In a typical **GI** list, **CHO-rich foods are rated on a scale from 0 to 100, according to their actual effect on blood glucose levels**. Internationally, glucose has a rating of 100, since it causes the greatest and most rapid rise in blood glucose levels, and all other foods are rated in comparison to glucose. It must, however, be noted that some GI testing has been published using white bread as the reference food, which is completely acceptable in the scientific world, but does create the impression that GI values from different sources differ. When looking up GI values, therefore, always make sure whether the reference food used is glucose or white bread. *The South African Glycemic Index and Load Guide* [available from the Glycemic Index Foundation of SA, (www.gifoundation.com), www.gabisteenkamp.co.za, your dietician, local bookstore, health shop or pharmacy] is one of the most reliable sources of the GI values of commonly eaten foods in South Africa. All the values published in the Guide are based on glucose as the reference food and it contains the most recent GI values of CHO-rich foods tested in SA and internationally. Since the GI is a rating of foods based on their actual effect on blood glucose levels, instead of on assumptions, it is much more accurate to use in the regulation of blood glucose levels.

Using the GI concept, those with diabetes and those suffering from other blood glucose control problems **[low blood sugar, i.e. hypoglycaemia, hyperinsulinaemia and insulin resistance, polycystic ovarian syndrome (PCOS), candidiasis, chronic fatigue syndrome (CFS), fibromyalgia syndrome (FMS), and children with Attention Deficit (Hyperactivity) Disorder (AD(H)D)]**, as well as **sportsmen**, can all optimise their blood glucose control.

Total and LDL cholesterol, and serum triglyceride levels and blood pressure can be lowered if the GI concept is used in combination with lower fat eating, and HDL (the 'good') cholesterol levels may be increased. For those who want to lose weight, the increased satiety and the fact that less insulin (a fat storer) is secreted, result in better fat loss. For a simple and comprehensive weight management book based on these principles, see *Eat Smart and Stay Slim: the GI Diet* (Tafelberg, 2003).

Even people suffering from **cancer, gout and irritable bowel syndrome (IBS)** can benefit from lower fat eating and the GI concept, although they should consult a dietician as some other adjustments will have to be made to their diets (see www.gifoundation.com for a list of dieticians who use the GI concept). Foods with a low GI release glucose slowly and steadily into the blood stream and do not overstimulate insulin secretion. High insulin levels are implicated in many lifestyle diseases: high blood pressure, high cholesterol and triglyceride levels, diabetes, hypoglycaemia, obesity, PCOS and heart disease.

Apart from being **lower GI**, all the recipes in this book are also **lower in fat**. Fat, especially saturated fat, is the main dietary cause of heart disease and high cholesterol, high blood pressure, being overweight and cancer, and also plays a major role in the development of hyperinsulinaemia, insulin resistance and gout. In addition, a high fat intake aggravates IBS and it also results in the body's insulin working less effectively, which may play a role in the development of reactive hypoglycaemia and eventually diabetes. Furthermore, it was found that it is fat and not really CHO (starches, vegetables, fruit, and sugars) that is fattening. It takes no effort for the body to turn dietary fat into body fat, whereas it takes a lot of effort and energy to convert CHO and protein into body fat. Thin people mostly consume a lower fat diet that is high in CHO and moderate in protein. Fat people eat high fat diets. Not more than 30% of total energy in our diet should come from fat. In this book we have heeded that recommendation and the fat content of every meal serving is kept as close to 10 g of fat (or below) as possible. If you would like more detailed information on the amount and type of fat per portion/day, consult our weight management book, *Eat Smart and Stay Slim*, and consult a dietician who can then advise and support you as you walk the path of weight management.

How the Glycemic Index is determined

The blood glucose response (BGR) to glucose or white bread (reference foods) of at least ten people, is measured. This is done on three different occasions for every person and the average value is the BGR of that person. The BGR to glucose is given a value of 100 and when white bread has been used as reference food, it has to be calibrated against glucose. Glucose is absorbed quickly and generally causes the greatest and most rapid rise in blood glucose of all foods. Blood glucose responses of all other carbohydrate (CHO) foods are also measured by actual blood tests in the same ten people per test food and rated in comparison to glucose for that specific person. The mean GI of the food for the group is allocated the GI value that can be applied to the general population. One could say that the GI of a food represents its blood glucose raising ability. Often the GI of a given food is not what one would expect. For example, the GI of South African brown bread is 81, whereas the mean GI of sweetened low-fat fruit yoghurt is only 33. For this reason all CHO-containing foods need to be tested in order to determine their GI.

By guessing the GI of a food, one could be very far out. The GI values of over 800 foods have been determined worldwide and more foods are being tested on a weekly basis, overseas as well as in South Africa. For a complete reference guide on the GI and GL values of foods commonly used in South Africa, see *The South African Glycemic Index and Load Guide* by Gabi Steenkamp and Liesbet Delport, which is available from the Glycemic Index Foundation of SA (www.gifoundation.com), www.gabisteenkamp.co.za, your dietician, local bookstore, health shop or pharmacy.

Factors that influence the Glycemic Index (GI)

Ongoing studies are revealing that the body's responses to foods are much more complex than originally anticipated. The following factors have an influence on the digestion and absorption of CHO, and thus on the GI of CHO-rich food, which is the measure, on a numerical scale, of how CHO-containing foods affect blood sugar levels.

The degree of starch gelatinisation Gelatinisation of starches occurs when the starchy food is exposed to liquid and/or heat (i.e. cooking). When potatoes are boiled, the heat and water expand the hard compact granules (which usually make raw potatoes difficult to digest) into swollen granules. Some granules even burst and free the individual starch molecules, which means they are easier to digest, (remember that starch is a string of glucose molecules.) The same happens when a sauce is thickened with flour or cornflour. The water binds with the starch in the presence of heat and gelatinises the flour, making it easier to digest. For this reason many confectionery items that contain sugar have a lower GI than those without. The sugar binds with some of the water, preventing it from binding with the flour and thereby limiting gelatinisation. The less a starch is gelatinised, the more slowly it is digested and absorbed and the lower the GI.

Particle size Intact grains, such as whole wheat, whole corn, whole rye, whole oats (groats) and whole barley, have much lower GI values than flours made from the same grains, because they have to be chewed and take longer to digest.

Processing Milling, beating, liquidising, grinding, mixing, mashing and refining foods raises the GI of that food by making it more easily available to the body. For this reason we limit the amount of beating and liquidising in the recipes.

The chemical composition of the starch Starches, such as rice, can have different types of starch structures, which affect their digestibility. Some types of rice, such as basmati and Tastic rice, have a higher amylose content. Amylose is made up of long, straight chains of glucose molecules packed closely together that exclude water and are therefore more difficult to digest. Other types of rice have a higher amylopectin content. These are branched chains of glucose molecules that are more open, hydrate more easily, are much easier to digest and thus have a higher GI. Rice that contains predominantly amylose (e.g. Tastic white rice) is inclined to be a loose cooked rice, whereas rice that contains predominantly amylopectin is inclined to be a more sticky cooked rice (e.g . arborio, risotto rice).

The type and content fibre Foods containing soluble fibre, such as oat bran, oats that are not processed too much, legumes (beans, peas and lentils), citrus and deciduous fruits, have a GI-lowering effect, as they make the stomach contents more viscous and delay gastric emptying. Insoluble fibre, such as that found in digestive bran, has very little effect on the digestibility of the CHO foods it is found in. Thus foods containing wheat (digestive) bran do not have a lower GI than those foods without the bran, unless the digestive bran is used in large quantities, e.g. in Hi-Fibre cereal. Brown bread and white bread have similar GI values and so do refined and unrefined mealie-meal. However, some insoluble fibres, e.g. fibre found in sugar beet and ispaghula, do have a GI-lowering effect, as they have a greater water-holding capacity than digestive bran, which helps to slow down digestion.

SUGAR **Sugar may lower the GI** of foods that have a very high GI, because sugar has a lower GI than many starches. A good example of this is Rice Krispies, which have a high GI. When they are sugar-coated, the GI is lower and thus Strawberry Pops have a lower GI than Rice Krispies! Likewise, sugar-free Weet-Bix has a higher GI than regular Weet-Bix, which contains sugar. Sugar can also lower the GI of baked goods (refer to p.11).

PROTEIN AND FAT The presence of protein and fat in food may lower the GI due to the interaction of these nutrients with each other and with CHO, since both proteins and fats slow down the rate at which food leaves the stomach. However, it is not advisable to eat too much protein or fat. Protein tends to wear out the body's insulin; and fat (especially saturated fat) has the effect of decreasing the effectiveness of insulin. Protein also overtaxes the kidneys and an overconsumption of protein can lead to osteoporosis, arthritis and gout.

ANTINUTRIENTS Phytates, lectins, saponins and polyphenols (tannins) normally slow digestion and thereby decrease the GI. These are normal constituents of many vegetables, legumes, fruit and bran.

ACIDITY The more acid a food, the lower the GI of that food, as acids also slow down gastric emptying. Naturally fermented sorghum porridge, for example, has a higher GI than cooked sorghum porridge to which an acid like vinegar or lemon juice has been added. The more tart fruits also have lower GI values. Sourdough breads, e.g. sourdough rye bread, have a lower GI value than regular rye bread, due to the presence of organic acids or salts, e.g. sodium propionate, which also slow down gastric emptying.

COOKING, Cooking, which increases the digestibility of food, usually has the effect of raising the GI of that food.

RESISTANT STARCH (RS) This type of starch resists digestion in the small intestine and passes into the large intestine, where it acts like fibre, is fermented by the colonic microflora and promotes the synthesis of short-chain fatty acids (SCFAs), which have many health benefits. There are three types: RS1 (in whole or partly ground grains, seeds, cereals and legumes); RS2 (in some raw starch granules, e.g. potato and green banana); and RS3 (retrograded starch). Retrograded starch develops in some cooked and cooled down starches, especially mealiemeal and samp. Thus cooked, cooled down maize porridge has a lower GI than the hot freshly prepared porridge, because the body has difficulty in digesting the retrograded starch that develops when some cooked starches are cooled down.

SPEED OF EATING Studies have shown that blood glucose levels rise less rapidly when eating more slowly.

The Glycemic Load (GL)

There is a new concept that 'fine tunes' the GI concept, called the Glycemic Load (GL). It addresses the concern about rating carbohydrate (CHO) foods as either 'good' or 'bad' on the basis of their GI. There is no such thing as good or bad CHO food; all foods can fit the bill! It all depends on when you eat it, how much you eat and with what you combine it. Although low GI food is usually the preferred choice, a high GI sports drink is perfect during and after a marathon, as a low GI drink during/after intense exercise could in fact result in hypoglycaemia.

The GL of a **specific food portion** is an expression of how much impact ('oomph'), or power, the food will have in affecting blood glucose levels. **It is calculated by taking the percentage of the food's CHO content per portion and multiplying it by its GI value.**

$$GL = \frac{\text{CHO content per portion} \times \text{GI}}{100}$$

It is thus a measure that incorporates both the quantity and quality of the dietary CHO consumed. Some fruits and vegetables, for example, have higher GI values and might be perceived as 'bad'. However, considering the amount of CHO per portion, the GL is low. This means that their effect on blood glucose levels would be minimal. Let us consider a few examples:

- The GI of watermelon is high (GI=72), but the GL of one serving of watermelon (150 g or 1/4 thick slice) is low (GL= 7), because the amount of CHO in this serving size is minimal, as watermelon contains a lot of water. However, watermelon juice has a high GL, because it has a high GI and the amount of CHO in a cup of watermelon juice (250 ml) is much more, as fruit juice is a concentrated source of CHO. Should you, however, indulge in watermelon and eat four cups of it, it will also have a high GL, as the GI is high and you will consume a lot of CHO.
- The GI of apples is 38 and the GL of one medium apple is 5. This means that eating one apple will have little effect on blood glucose levels. However, if you eat a whole 500 g packet of dried apples, its GL would be 50, which means that it will have a huge effect on your blood glucose levels, despite it being low GI, as dried fruit is a concentrated source of CHO. The GL therefore shows us how important it is to watch portion sizes.
- The GI of SA white or brown bread is high (GI > 70) and the GL of two slices (2 x 40 g slices of bread contain 40 g of CHO) is also high (GL > 30), because the amount of CHO in a hand-cut slice of refined bread is substantial. This means that a sandwich made with two slices of brown or white bread will have a marked effect on blood glucose levels as the bread will have an 'oomph' or

impact of about 30. However, should you use one **thin** slice of bread as part of a mixed meal containing low GI baked beans, ham and other salad vegetables, the GL of the meal will be lower and more acceptable (GL=22). Note that the two slices of refined bread on their own have a higher GL than a whole meal, in which only one thin slice of bread is used in combination with other low GI foods.

- The GL of one slice of seed loaf bread is only 9. You can therefore also lower the GL of a meal that basically consists of a sandwich from about 30 to about 20, by using heavier bread instead of brown or white bread. This means that regular refined bread will spike blood glucose levels (higher GL), and the seed loaf will not (lower GL), but it still does not mean that you can overindulge on seed loaf. Fortunately seed loaf bread is more filling and it is not as easy to overindulge in this, as it is to overindulge in brown or white bread.
- In addition, the GL of a roll (equivalent to two slices of bread) is over 20, and the GL of a bagel (equivalent to three slices of bread) is over 30! Imagine what this does to blood glucose levels, as the GI is also high!
- From this we can see that it is quite acceptable to include small amounts of high GI foods in a meal, as long as the bulk of the meal contains lower GI CHO foods (vegetables, fruit, low GI starches, legumes and/or dairy).

New evidence associates high GL meals with an increased risk of heart disease and diabetes, especially in overweight and insulin resistant persons. Therefore, it is advisable to restrict the GL of a typical meal to between 20 and 25 as far as possible, but definitely below 30. The GL of a typical snack should preferably be about 10, but definitely below 15, but if your meals are all close to 30, the total of all your snacks should be no more than 10! This means that you would have to eat only fruit for snacks, in order to keep your total daily GL below 100, as the GL of a portion of fruit is usually below 10.

What does it mean when a food has a low GL?

A CHO food that has a low GL will have a small impact on blood glucose levels, as it is either not high in CHO and/or has a low GI, so you would have to eat quite a lot of it before it would have any effect on your blood glucose levels. In other words, eating any one of the muffins contained in this lower GI, lower fat recipe book or in *Eating for Sustained Energy 2*, should not raise your blood glucose levels significantly, as they have a lower GL.

Having a **low GL and a low GI** is doubly beneficial. A food with a low GI and very little 'push' or 'power' (GL) behind it will naturally have a very small impact on blood glucose levels, such as low GI vegetables (tomatoes, lettuce, cucumber, onions, asparagus, mushrooms, etc.). It follows then that these foods are also not very effective at lowering the GI of high GI foods such as white or brown bread, as they are very low in CHO.

Remember: the GI indicates the extent to which a food will raise blood glucose levels, whereas the GL indicates the 'power' or 'push' behind the GI.

High GI and High GL means trouble – blood glucose levels will shoot up. This means the food in question will have a lot of 'power' behind the already high GI, and even a small portion will have a marked effect. Examples of this are cooked mealiemeal and potatoes and the regular SA bread mentioned above. These foods are high in CHO and therefore a small portion already contains a lot of CHO. In addition, they have high GI values, which aggravate the effect on blood glucose levels.

Low GI combined with a high GL will also impact on blood glucose levels. Remember that the GL is based on the quantity of CHO in a food, and represents the GI in portion size. So the more CHO there is in a food, the higher its GL, i.e. the more the impact on blood glucose levels. So even low GI foods, if eaten in large quantities, can affect blood glucose levels quite significantly, especially if they are concentrated sources of CHO, e.g. most cakes, dried fruit and dried fruit rolls, fruit juices, crisps, chocolates, etc. Crisps and chocolates are also high in fat and/or saturated fat, making them undesirable.

And lastly, a high GI food with a low GL will not necessarily affect blood glucose levels significantly. Good examples are the high GI vegetables (e.g.pumpkin). They contain only a little CHO and therefore, in normal portion sizes, will not impact on blood glucose levels even though they have a high GI, as the impact on blood glucose levels is not significant. The proviso is, though, that they are not eaten with other high GI or GL foods and that they are not consumed in huge quantities.

Please note that the GL of the starch component of most of our low GI breakfasts (such as those in all our lower GI, lower fat recipe books) is about 15, the GL of the starch component of most low GI light meals in our recipe books is between 15 and 20, and the GL of most low GI main meals is about 20 to 25. This means that three meals per day should add up to a GL of between 55 and 70, as most people will add salad and/or fruit to breakfasts and light meals, which also contribute to the GL. This leaves 30 to 45 GL points for snacks and drinks, as most of these have a GL of 10 to 15, except for fruit, which has a GL of below 10. The aim is to keep the total GL per day under 100, especially for persons with diabetes and other lifestyle diseases and even more so for those who need to lose weight.

How to make the Glycemic Index work for you

All foods that have a GI of 55 or less are **slow release carbohydrates (CHOs)** and are the best choices for most people. This is particularly true for inactive people, the overweight, sportsmen and women before exercise, as well as persons suffering from diabetes, hypoglycaemia, hyperinsulinaemia, insulin resistance, candidiasis, PCOS, ME, FMS, inflammatory diseases such as arthritis, high triglycerides and AD(H)D. Slow-release CHOs do not result in a sudden high rise in blood glucose levels, and for this reason they keep blood glucose levels steady for several hours. **They are called low GI foods.** Low GI foods are more satisfying and do not cause the release of as much insulin as high GI foods do and therefore also prevent the reactive drop in blood glucose levels. High GI foods elicit a huge insulin response, the body's way of coping with the sudden, sharp rise in blood glucose levels, after high GI foods have been eaten. Often the insulin response is too much and blood glucose levels fall rapidly below the starting point, a condition known as hypoglycaemia. This swing from very high to very low blood glucose levels, due to hyperinsulinaemia, is now believed to be a contributing factor to most of the so-called lifestyle diseases.

These diseases are actually caused by high insulin levels in the blood and could be prevented, to a large extent, if the general public were to consume lower fat, lower GI foods most of the time and reserve higher GI foods for during and/or after exercise. Researchers regard all foods with a GI of 62 or below as 'safe', even though the cut-off point for a low GI food is 55.

Intermediate and high GI foods, on the other hand, are very useful for sportsmen and women, during and after exercise. **Intermediate GI foods are those with a GI ranging from 56 to 69 and release glucose moderately quickly into the blood stream.**

They are the best choice in the following cases:

- After low-intensity exercise of short duration, e.g. a 30-minute walk
- the morning after an evening of prolonged and vigorous exercise
- in persons with diabetes, directly after moderate activity, such as training in a gym for an hour, and during and immediately after exercise lasting longer than 1 to 1½ hours.

Foods with a GI of 70+ are fast-release CHO and are called **high GI foods**. High GI foods are excellent for the prevention of fatigue and hypoglycaemia in healthy sportsmen within 30 to 60 minutes of completing moderate to high-intensity exercise lasting at least one hour, and during and within 30 to 60 minutes of completing exercise lasting more than 1 to 1½ hours. High GI foods should, however, be avoided by people with diabetes under normal circumstances, but could perhaps be consumed during and after strenuous exercise lasting 90 minutes or more, after careful experimentation. Small quantities of high GI foods are also useful during a low blood glucose 'attack' (the so-called hypo), but it is better to aim to prevent low blood glucose levels than to treat them.

Any person who would like to have sustained energy during exercise, should not consume high GI foods before exercise or when he or she is inactive, but rather have low GI foods.

Healthy eating

In South Africa we now have Food-Based Dietary Guidelines that are really easy to understand and implement on a daily basis (see below). By simply applying the first guideline – eating a variety of foods at every meal – you ensure a wide variety of nutrients, which in turn optimises nutrition. Applying all of them would optimise your nutritional intake and the recipes in this book and *Eating for Sustained Energy 2* do just that.

The South African Dietary Guidelines

1. Enjoy a variety of foods.
2. Be active.
3. Make lower GI starchy foods the basis of most meals.
4. Eat plenty of vegetables and fruits every day.
5. Eat cooked dried beans, peas, lentils and soya regularly.
6. Lower fat chicken, fish, meat, milk, yoghurt, cheese or eggs can be eaten daily.
7. Eat fats (especially saturated fats) sparingly.
8. Use salt sparingly and limit salty foods.
9. Drink lots of clean, safe water.
10. If you drink alcohol, drink sensibly, i.e. not more than one to two drinks per day.
11. Eat and drink foods containing sugar sparingly and not between meals.

Breakfast is the most important meal of the day and 'sets the stage', in a manner of speaking, for the rest of the day. This is particularly true for people with diabetes. A well-balanced lower GI, lower fat breakfast stabilises blood glucose levels, so that by the time lunch time comes around, you are only just hungry again and have not had a blood glucose surge or slump all morning. In other words, the body has been able to operate with optimum fuel levels all morning. A high GI and/or high fat breakfast can result in shakiness, fatigue and irritability all day long, unless a substantial amount of exercise was done before breakfast and the high GI breakfast was consumed within 30 to 60 minutes of completing the exercise. The excess insulin released in response to the surge in blood glucose from the high GI food does not happen after exercise, due to the action of the enzyme, glycogen resynthetase, which is very active after exercise and is responsible for replacing the glycogen lost from the muscles and liver during exercise.

Breakfast

We would like, therefore, to recommend that those who don't exercise before breakfast eat a hearty lower fat, lower GI breakfast to keep blood glucose levels stable for the rest of the morning. Breakfast should contain lower GI carbohydrate (CHO) foods, e.g. a lower GI muffin or cereal or porridge (see GI list on page 24), some protein, e.g. lower fat cheese, and a little fat (already in the muffin and cheese). Fruit can either be added to the breakfast or eaten as a mid-morning snack. See pages 26–36 for breakfast ideas.

Lunch/light meals

The modern trend today is not to eat lunch. This results in very low blood glucose levels before suppertime, and the result is often a raid on the fridge. We'd like to emphasise, therefore, the importance of eating a lower fat, lower GI lunch, consisting mainly of lower GI starch, e.g. seed loaf (see GI list on page 24 for more lower GI options), together with a salad. Add to this a little lower fat protein or dairy, e.g. lean meat/fish/chicken/ cheese/ eggs/legumes, and a minimum of fat, e.g. spread avocado on your bread instead of margarine. End off the meal with low GI fruit or keep the fruit for a snack later on. For lunch time suggestions see the sections on light meals (page 34), salads (page 44) and soups (page 38).

Supper/dinner

The bulk of the evening meal should, once again, be lower GI carbohydrate (CHO), in the form of vegetables and starch. Approximately half of your plate should be filled with vegetables, one-quarter with low GI starch (see GI list on page 24) and only one-quarter with lower fat protein (lean meat, fish or chicken; or beans, peas, lentils or texturised vegetable protein). Vegetarians can use low-fat milk, yoghurt, cheese, legumes or nuts as protein, but should remember that nuts are 50% fat and the intake of nuts should therefore be limited, even though they contain mainly healthier fat. [See main meals (pages 60–102) and light meals (page 54)].

Eating high GI CHO for supper after a day of non-activity, could result in reactive low blood glucose levels a few hours later or during the night. People with diabetes who eat high GI starches for supper will invariably have elevated blood glucose levels above 10 mmol/l about one hour after supper and elevated fasting blood glucose levels the next morning, i.e. over 7 mmol/l, both of which are undesirable. Eating protein with higher GI CHO will reduce the effect of the CHO on blood glucose levels, but not as effectively as when eating higher GI CHO with protein that contains CHO and has an overall low GI, e.g. low-fat milk, yoghurt and legumes. (See discussion on GL on page 13). Eating large portions of protein and fat, such as fatty red meat, can also result in high blood glucose levels the next morning, especially in those who have diabetes.

Fibre

Most South Africans do not come close to eating the recommended 30 to 40 g fibre per day. Low fibre intakes have been linked to high cholesterol levels, high blood pressure, diabetes (since most high-fibre foods – although not all of them – are also low GI and, in addition, fibre also improves insulin sensitivity), spastic colon, gall stones and cancer, especially colon and breast cancer.

Fibre is the indigestible part of plant foods, and is therefore not found in animal protein or fats. It moves almost untouched through the alimentary canal until it reaches the colon, adding bulk and softness to the stool for easy evacuation. There are two types of fibre: water-soluble fibre, found in oats, oat bran, barley, legumes, pasta, mealies, deciduous and citrus fruits and some vegetables, and insoluble fibre found in digestive bran, brown and whole-wheat bread, whole wheat (sold as Weet-Rice or pearled wheat), brown rice, etc. Both play a vital role in gut health and should be consumed every day.

Foods that contain mostly soluble fibre also have a low GI. If eaten regularly instead of high fat, high GI foods, they can protect against Type 2 Diabetes, since these foods do not overstimulate insulin secretion. Constant over-stimulation of insulin secretion by eating high fat, high GI, low-fibre foods, may lead to the depletion of the beta cells of the pancreas (which are responsible for producing insulin) and the onset of Type 2 Diabetes. Soluble fibre also binds cholesterol and is therefore effective in lowering cholesterol levels.

Although we include some low-fibre foods in the GI list on page 24, so that you can know which foods are low, intermediate and high GI, we want to encourage you rather to choose a higher fibre product that is also lower in fat and GI, instead of the refined counterpart.

The sweet truth about sugar

When one hears the word sugar, one automatically thinks of table sugar, the sweetness we add to tea and coffee. However, there is much more to sugar than that. Chemically, sugar is known as sucrose, but technically there are many different types of sugar. The sugar in fruit, for example, can be fructose, sucrose, glucose, or a combination of any of these; the sugar in milk is known as lactose, and so on. A sugar-free food may, in fact, not be sugar free at all – merely free of sucrose and not necessarily low GI or lower in kilojoules (kJ). New SA legislation may not allow for a food to be called 'sugar free' if it contains any one of the different types of sugars listed below, unless the GI has been tested.

A. SUGARS: MONO- AND DISACCHARIDES: These consist of either one or two molecules of different sugars and have varying effects on blood glucose levels, or the GI of the food containing them. Some (low GI) are absorbed more slowly and steadily than others, which can be absorbed really rapidly (high GI).

The following 'sugars' individually have a low GI, but contain just as many kJ as table sugar: fructose, Krystar 300 (fructose), Fructofin C (fructose – GMO free), Dolcresun Q0 & Q2 (a syrup that's very high in fructose) and lactose (milk sugar). The following 'sugars' have an intermediate GI and contain as many kJ as the above: sucrose (table sugar) and invert sugar. The following 'sugars' are high GI and contain as many kJ as table sugar: glucose, dextrose, maltose and maltotriose.

B. Sugar alcohols/polyols (1 to 2 molecules): These also consist of two molecules of different sugars, but are, in addition, bound to an alcohol molecule. This makes them more difficult to digest, which means the sugar is released into the blood stream more slowly, resulting in a low GI value. A certain percentage of these sugars are not digested at all and thus they contain less kJ than regular sugars. They can, however, cause gastric discomfort (flatulence, cramping and/or diarrhoea), if taken in excess. Examples of sugar alcohols are: lactitol, xylitol, isomalt, maltitol, sorbitol and mannitol.

C. Oligosaccharides (3 to 9 molecules): These consist of more than two molecules of different sugars and can be either low or high GI.

- Indigestible oligosaccharides (low GI) are not digested at all, and the body deals with them as it would deal with fibre. All of them are therefore low GI and most of them are also kJ free, except for Sugalite, which contains about a third of the kJ of table sugar. These sugars ferment in the colon and form short chain fatty acids (SCFAs). This has certain health benefits, such as a reduction in fasting blood glucose, but they can also cause gastric discomfort if they are taken in excess (flatulence, cramping and/or diarrhoea). Examples of oligosaccharides include Frutafit HD, IQ and TEX, Inulin (FOS or fructo-oligosaccharides), polydextrose, Litesse Ultra (ultra-refined polydextrose), Litesse II (refined polydextrose), pyrodextrins, galacto-oligosaccharides, raffinose, stachyose and Sugalite.
- Some malto-oligosaccharides (high GI), such as maltodextrin, can be digested by our bodies, but contain as many kJ as table sugar and have a very high GI value, i.e. over 100!

D. Polysaccharides (> 10 molecules): These contain as many kJ as table sugar and most of them are high GI. Examples of these are dextrins – which are intermediate products in the hydrolysis of starch – and consist of shorter chains of glucose units, and glucose polymers or corn syrup solids, which are partially or fully hydrolysed cornstarch.

E. Non-nutritive or artificial sweeteners: These are the only sweeteners that are free of energy or kJ. Do not eat them too freely, though, as we are not sure of their long-term effects on the human body. Examples: saccharine, cyclamates, acesulfame K, aspartame and sucralose.

So now you know how to distinguish between the effects of different 'sugars' on blood glucose levels, as well as their kJ value.

If any of the high GI 'sugars' listed above are one of the first three ingredients in a product, beware! The GI might just be high!

Conditions that benefit from the lower GI lower fat way of eating

Diabetes mellitus

Diabetes is on the increase at a rate of 11% a year and is reaching epidemic proportions. This is due in part to the high GI, high fat diet the general public consumes, as well as an increasingly sedentary lifestyle, stress and smoking. There are two types of diabetes: Type 1 Diabetes (10% of diabetics) and Type 2 Diabetes (90% of diabetics). In Type I Diabetes, the beta cells of the pancreas are unable to produce insulin and the onset is usually sudden. A pre-existing genetic component is usually present, as well as a precipitating factor, e.g. a viral infection or in some cases certain proteins, which can spark off an immune response. Often it is the trigger that is the proverbial last straw for becoming diabetic, e.g. an infection, stress or trauma. These do not, however, cause diabetes. The classic symptoms, especially of Type 1 Diabetes, include chronic thirst, chronic urination, chronic hunger and excessive weight loss in spite of consuming large quantities of food and drink. Type I diabetics need to inject insulin every day.

Type 2 Diabetes is less easy to diagnose and the onset is usually slow. Thirty percent of Type 2 diabetics already have complications at the time of diagnosis. Usually these people are overweight, have insulin resistance and already have high cholesterol and/or high triglycerides, as well as high blood pressure by the time diabetes is diagnosed. They often have no, or vague, symptoms, e.g. chronic infections, chronic fatigue, pain, cramps or a burning sensation in the legs and feet, shortness of breath, etc. Some of these people have a relative insulin deficiency and can be treated with diet and exercise alone, or diet, exercise and tablets. Others have an absolute insulin shortage and need to be treated with diet, exercise and insulin therapy. Early diagnosis is important, so have your blood glucose, blood lipids and blood pressure checked regularly irrespective of symptoms. The earlier diabetes is diagnosed and treated, the smaller the chances are of serious complications, e.g. blindness, kidney failure, amputations, heart attacks or stroke.

Modern treatment of diabetes

As with all new research, the GI has not been universally welcomed with open arms. It has its critics, most of whom cling to past assumptions. Unfortunately, they prefer to believe what they think should happen to a person's blood glucose in response to eating certain foods, rather than having to face what actually happens to blood glucose when carbohydrate (CHO) foods are eaten. Remember that the GI is a physiological measure of the body's response to a particular CHO.

Research conducted over the past 30 years in Canada, Australia, the United Kingdom, Italy, France, Denmark, the East and Far East, as well as South Africa, shows convincingly that many foods that were regarded as 'safe' on the traditional sugar free diet, actually raise diabetic persons' blood glucose levels higher than some ordinary foods that may contain a little sugar. Some of the foods previously regarded 'safe' elicit very high blood glucose increases and should rather be avoided. Many other foods that contain sugar, which persons with diabetes have had to avoid in the past, cause no major fluctuations in blood glucose levels. It does not, therefore, make sense to ban these foods for those with diabetes. If you consult the GI list (page 24), you will notice that South African brown bread has a high GI value, whereas sweetened fruit yoghurt has a low GI value. This means that one or two slices of brown bread, eaten as dry toast, for example, would result in a much greater blood glucose level rise than eating a small tub of sweetened fruit yoghurt.

The new lower fat, lower GI diet is much more effective in lowering and controlling blood glucose levels, because it is based on what happens to real people (diabetic and healthy persons) when they eat real food, in real life. Umpteen dieticians across the world have countless examples of how insulin and oral medication in individuals with diabetes was decreased – or even discontinued in some cases – since the lower GI, lower fat diet was followed. Many of these people had been on a sugar-free diet (and sometimes even low fat as well) for many years and could still not get their blood glucose readings to under 10 mmol/l. As soon as they started following the lower fat, lower GI diet, their readings dropped to below 10 mmol/l for the first time in years, **not by avoiding sugar, but by avoiding high fat, high GI foods**.

A high-fat diet also results in insulin working less effectively, which, in turn, can lead to a relative or absolute shortage of insulin, as well as hyperinsulinaemia and insulin resistance. This predisposes a person to all the lifestyle diseases (diabetes, heart disease, hypertension and obesity). The lower fat, lower GI diet is much more 'user friendly' than the traditional diabetic diet, because sugar is no longer completely forbidden. Portion control is also easier when eating slow release (lower GI), lower fat foods, as increased satiety helps to control how much is eaten. If you are overweight, however, you will have to watch portion sizes more carefully. This is the reason we give the number of portions of starch, protein, fat, etc., for every recipe, so that those who want or need to watch their weight can do so by sticking to the recommended number of portions given to them by a dietician. In addition, keeping to the number of servings recommended per dish at the top of every recipe, will also help with weight management. Larger portion sizes are, however, also given for those whose weight is normal or who need to carbo-load or gain weight.

Please note that all recipes in *Eating for Sustained Energy 1* are suitable for all persons with diabetes. Every meal consumed by an individual with diabetes should contain at least one low GI food (slow release CHO). If most of the foods in a meal are low GI, then intermediate and even small amounts of high GI foods can be added to the same meal. We have applied this principle in many of the recipes in this book, and have mentioned this in the Dieticians' notes provided with the recipes. For maximum reduction in blood glucose levels – especially if you have a fasting blood glucose value that is higher than 8 mmol/l and a random blood glucose value higher than 10 mmol/l – it is important to consume mainly low GI foods at every meal.

Hypoglycaemia (low blood sugar)

Hypoglycaemia results when blood glucose levels fall below normal levels (hypo = under and glycemia = blood sugar/glucose). Many people suffer from hypoglycaemia, not surprisingly since most of the foods that are freely available and consumed by the general public are high in fat and have a high GI value. The most common form of hypoglycaemia occurs after a meal or snack is eaten. This is called reactive hypoglycaemia. High GI foods (except when eaten during, or after exercise), result in a sharp increase in blood glucose levels within a short period of time, i.e. 15 to 30 minutes after ingestion. The human body then tries to rectify the situation by releasing insulin to counteract the threat of sustained high blood glucose levels. Insulin removes the glucose from the blood stream, often too enthusiastically, resulting in a rapid fall in blood glucose levels. This results in the typical stress-like symptoms of low blood sugar, i.e. tremors, heart palpitations, sweating, anxiety, irritability, sleepiness, weakness and shakiness, as well as the very common feeling of chronic fatigue. Hypoglycaemia can also affect mental function and lead to restlessness, irritability, poor concentration, visual disturbance, lethargy and drowsiness. These symptoms are clearly noticeable in non-diabetic persons during GI research done by scientists, especially if high GI foods are eaten.

The logical treatment for hypoglycaemia is to control the influx of glucose into the blood stream. Consuming mainly slow release carbohydrate (CHO) (low GI) at mealtimes and as snacks, one is able to ensure that a slow, but steady stream of glucose is released into the blood stream that will not trigger the release of huge surges of insulin. If, on top of eating high GI foods, one consumes a lot of fat, especially saturated fat (which causes the body's insulin to work less effectively), it is only a question of time before impaired glucose tolerance (the forerunner of Type 2 Diabetes) develops. The reason for this is that the beta cells of the pancreas (that produce insulin) become worn out by continually trying to correct the surges of glucose released into the blood when fast release CHO (high GI) are eaten, and the insulin that is released, cannot work properly due to the high-fat diet.

This can lead to hyperinsulinaemia (too much insulin in the blood, in response to the high blood glucose levels) and insulin resistance. Insulin resistance causes the body's cells to shut down (since they do not like to be drowned in insulin) and 'forget' that they are supposed to transfer the glucose from the blood stream into the body cells, in response to insulin. The results are high insulin, as well as high blood glucose levels. Other factors that can contribute to insulin resistance are genetic factors, inactivity, obesity and ageing. Hyperinsulinaemia, in turn, can lead to diabetes, hyperlipidaemia, hypertension and heart disease, as well as resistance to weight loss.

This whole vicious cycle needs to be broken before the body will start functioning properly again.

Follow these simple guidelines to prevent hypoglycaemia and all its nasty consequences:

- Eat regular meals and snacks, preferably every three hours.
- Include slow release CHO (low GI) at every meal or snack to keep blood glucose levels steady.
- Avoid eating fast release CHOs (high GI) on their own. Preferably avoid them altogether (see GI list on page 24), but if you have to eat a high GI CHO, always combine it with low GI CHO or at least with some protein and/or a little fat, or eat it after moderate exercise or during and after prolonged exercise. Eating high and low GI foods together yields an overall Intermediate GI, as explained previously. For lots of tips on food combining, see *The South African Glycemic Index and Load Guide* by Gabi Steenkamp and Liesbet Delport, available from the Glycemic Index Foundation of SA (www.gifoundation.com), www.gabisteenkamp.co.za, your dietitian, local bookstore, health shop or pharmacy.

Sport-induced hypoglycaemia

Hypoglycaemia or 'low blood sugar' occurring during or after sport, can happen when the sportsman or woman does not eat slow-release carbohydrate (CHO) foods (low GI) before exercise and either eats nothing during and/or after exercise, or eats slow-release CHO foods (low GI) after exercise or eats too long after exercise. To prevent this, low GI CHO (slow-release) should be eaten one to two hours before exercise in order to stabilise blood glucose and insulin levels during exercise. Higher GI beverages or food (fast-release CHO) should be consumed within the first 30–60 minutes after exercise lasting 60–90 minutes, and during and after exercise lasting longer than 60–90 minutes. Doing this keeps blood glucose levels steady and replenishes glycogen used by the muscles.

Coronary heart disease (CHD)

In westernised South Africans, 40% of deaths in the economically active age group (25 to 64 years), result from chronic diseases of lifestyle, such as cancer, hypertension (high blood pressure), diabetes, stroke and coronary heart disease (CHD). Of all these, CHD causes the greatest number of deaths. In fact, CHD is the number one killer in South Africa and many other countries of the world today. The development of CHD is a slow process and starts with fatty deposit build-up on the inner walls of the arteries of the heart and brain. This may lead to narrowing of the arteries (atherosclerosis) that supply the heart and the brain with oxygen. When the blood cannot get through any more, the person suffers a heart attack or stroke. Often a part of the heart muscle dies or a section of the body is paralysed (stroke), if the patient is lucky enough to survive. The frightening thing is that, as excess cholesterol slowly constricts and clogs your arteries, you won't necessarily suffer any pain or discomfort, except maybe fatigue and shortness of breath. Some people experience chest pain (angina), but for many, the first warning sign could be a heart attack or stroke.

Risk factors

A number of factors contribute to an increased risk of CHD, including high blood cholesterol levels, high blood pressure, being overweight, diabetes, smoking, stress, a lack of exercise and a family history of CHD. An increasing number of people have also been found to suffer from high levels of blood triglycerides (another type of fat in the blood that predisposes one to diabetes). To lower such higher triglyceride levels, a lower fat, low GL diet is recommended. High levels of blood cholesterol and triglycerides, high blood pressure, diabetes, weight problems, gout and cancer are all influenced by the quantity of fat (especially saturated fat and 'processed' fat) in our diet. Higher saturated fat intakes result in more LDL cholesterol, which is the dangerous cholesterol. Oxidised LDL cholesterol is laid down in the arteries most easily, and that is why it is important to prevent oxidation of LDL cholesterol by eating lots of fresh fruit and vegetables. Saturated fat also causes the body to retain dietary cholesterol, which makes saturated fat the number one culprit in raising blood cholesterol levels, not dietary cholesterol, as was previously thought. It can also reduce levels of the good HDL cholesterol, which is another reason saturated fat (animal fats) should be restricted. Fat, especially saturated fat, is also believed to be the main dietary promoter of cancer, as well as the main cause of extra body fat or obesity. Most of the foods South Africans love to eat are high in saturated fats and trans-fatty acids, another 'bad' fat. To name but a few: fatty meat such as lamb and mutton chops, dried sausage, fatty biltong, toasted sandwiches, pies and other confectionery such as cakes, tarts, biscuits, rusks and croissants, full-cream ice cream, chocolate, rich sauces, desserts and all deep-fried foods. Too much sodium, together with a high fat, high GI diet, too much alcohol and being overweight and inactive can aggravate high blood pressure. Smoking also plays a major role.

Treatment

It is, however, possible to eat most of these foods, provided they are the lower in fat, lower GI and lower sodium versions. This book is full of delicious, normal recipes that are low in total fat, saturated fat, trans-fatty acids, GI, GL and sodium and will not cause fatty deposit build-up on the inner walls of arteries.

We decided rather to recommend the use of canola or olive oil, which are both high in mono-unsaturated fatty acids (MUFAs), in the recipes, as research has shown that large quantities of omega-6 polyunsaturated fatty acids (PUFAs), especially from plant origin – e.g. polyunsaturated soft (tub) margarine, sunflower oil, cottonseed oil, sunflower seeds, walnuts, etc. – can give rise to nasty reactive chemicals called free radicals. These are implicated in heart disease, cancer and ageing, and can lessen the more beneficial HDL cholesterol. Polyunsaturated fats (omega-3s) which occur in fatty fish, e.g. pilchards, trout, tuna (packed in water or brine), sardines and salmon (without the oil), mackerel (in water), etc. seem to be much, healthier, since they lower fibrinogen levels in the blood, which slows down blood clotting, and also helps to increase the good HDL cholesterol. We recommend that fatty fish be eaten once or twice a week.

MUFAs, which are found in olive oil, canola oil, macadamia oil, olives, avocados, peanut butter and raw unsalted nuts (except brazil nuts), decrease bad cholesterol and raise good HDL cholesterol levels. HDL cholesterol is responsible for the removal of the 'bad' fats from the arteries, by transporting them to the liver to be excreted. HDL cholesterol levels may be increased by exercise, a low GI diet, moderate use of red wine (one to two wine glasses per day) and using mainly MUFAs and omega-3 PUFAs as sources of fat.

Fibre, especially soluble fibre (which happens to be in many low GI foods, such as legumes, barley and oat bran) also plays an important role in decreasing the risk of CHD. Soluble fibre binds cholesterol in the alimentary canal, thereby reducing serum cholesterol, especially the bad LDL cholesterol. For this reason we have included many recipes with one or other legume or lower GI oats/oat bran as an ingredient. The plant sterols in legumes are very effective at decreasing the risk of heart disease and oat products are the richest source of soluble fibre. If you want to reduce the risk of CHD, you will have to exercise more, stop smoking, decrease your intake of salt, lose weight or avoid becoming overweight and eat a lower fat, lower GI diet.

Attention Deficit Hyperactivity Disorder (ADHD) or Attention Deficit Disorder (ADD)

For years it was believed that ADHD and ADD were caused, or at least aggravated, by the consumption of sugar. Sugar was believed to cause hypoglycaemia, and it was recently found that hyperactivity and/or ADHD and hypoglycaemia are interrelated. Now that we know that it is high GI foods that cause hypoglycaemia, we recommend that children who suffer from ADHD or ADD should avoid high GI foods (such as refined bread, most refined cereals, cold drinks, energy drinks and sweets that are high in glucose), rather than just avoiding foods that are high in sugar.

Why AD(H)D and hypoglycaemia are interrelated

Many children with ADHD or ADD crave high GI carbohydrates (CHOs). All high GI foods cause a rapid rise in blood glucose levels, which results in the pancreas pouring out insulin in an attempt to bring the blood glucose down to a normal level. In many people, and some children who suffer from ADHD or ADD, the body pours out too much insulin, resulting in too much glucose being drawn out of the blood, and the blood sugar level falling below normal. The end result is a hypoglycaemic attack with the accompanying irritability, lack of concentration and poor sleeping habits. (See the section on hypoglycaemia, page 17, for other symptoms that are usually caused by eating high GI foods.) When high GI foods are eaten for breakfast, a hypoglycaemic attack may occur 1 to 1½ hours later – before first break at school, and at a time when the brain should still be receiving a steady supply of energy from the food that was eaten two to three hours before, as is the case with low GI foods. If high GI foods are eaten at break (which often happens, since the child feels the need to compensate for the tired feeling by eating, usually another high GI food), the same scenario can repeat itself later in the morning. This, we think, is the reason these children struggle to concentrate. The brain's fuel is constantly undergoing huge swings and this is not conducive to thinking or behaving in a normal manner.

Evidence is starting to emerge that an adverse food reaction may also cause a significant drop in blood glucose levels. The endocrine (glandular) system overreacts and this may cause a sudden rise – and later a drop – in blood glucose levels. It is hypothesised that, by constantly eating certain foods, the enzymes needed to digest and metabolise the food are over-extended, to the point where an allergy to that particular food may develop. When an allergic reaction develops, a chemical called histamine can be produced. Histamine causes the adrenal glands to excrete adrenalin, which stimulates the liver to convert stored sugar (glycogen) into blood glucose. This sudden rise in blood sugar levels can also cause the pancreas to pour out insulin. The end result is a hypoglycaemic attack. If a child is allergic to a specific food, it can also cause hypoglycaemia and swings in blood glucose levels and moods. The fact that allergy to a specific foodstuff affects blood glucose levels has been confirmed by GI tests that have been carried out and we have also observed this in some of our patients.

Caffeine can also cause hyperactivity initially and hypoglycaemia with the resultant symptoms later. This is due to the fact that caffeine also stimulates the adrenal glands to excrete adrenalin, which stimulates the liver to pour glucose into the blood stream. This sudden rise in blood sugar levels can once again cause the pancreas to pour out insulin. The end result is a hypoglycaemic attack.

Treatment

In light of the above, we recommend that all high GI foods, caffeine and any food to which a child with ADHD or ADD is allergic, should be avoided, as all of these foods may induce hypoglycaemia. If low GI foods are eaten most of the time, but especially for breakfast (since breakfast sets the tone for the rest of the day), the brain receives a steady supply of energy from the food. This is because low GI foods result neither in a sudden, nor a substantial rise in blood glucose levels and consequently no sudden drop in blood glucose levels, due to the oversecretion of insulin. Low GI foods keep blood glucose levels even, enabling the child to concentrate better.

Examples of low GI breakfast foods are lower GI oats, whole-wheat ProNutro, high-fibre cereal, deciduous fruits and fruit yoghurt, to name but a few. (See GI list on page 24 and the breakfast section on pages 26–36 for more ideas.)

It is also advisable to keep these children away from flavourings, preservatives, and especially colourings, since the latter were found to inhibit the uptake of a very important neurotransmitter, vital for the transmission of messages. Foods and medicines containing salicylate should also preferably be avoided, since they are chemically related to the former three additives and can interfere with the transmission of messages in the brain. Children who suffer from ADHD or ADD also benefit greatly from additional essential fatty acids (especially omega-3 fatty acids, which enhance the transfer of messages in the brain), as well as certain vitamins and minerals. For more information, consult a dietician who specialises in the treatment of ADHD and ADD. See GIFSA's website at www.gifoundation.com for a list of dieticians who use the GI in their treatment of patients.

The only exception to the low GI rule is during, and especially after exercise, but more about that in the section on sports nutrition (page 21). Please note that all the recipes in *Eating for Sustained Energy 1* are suitable for children with ADHD and ADD, provided the child does not suffer from an allergy to one of the ingredients, and is not salicylate sensitive.

Weight management

For a complete guide to effective weight management see *Eat Smart and Stay Slim: the GI Diet* by Liesbet Delport and Gabi Steenkamp (Tafelberg 2003).

Follow a lower fat diet

For some or other unknown reason, carbohydrates (CHOs) have, for the last 20 to 30 years, been labelled fattening. Although research done in the last fifteen years has disproved this over and over again, CHOs are still struggling to get rid of the 'fattening' label. CHO has actually been found to stimulate its own metabolism, which means that if you eat more of it, your body will merely burn more. This is, however, not the case with fat. Dietary fat has been found to simply slip into body fat unchanged, proving that it does not stimulate its own metabolism. If one eats a lot of a certain type of fat (such as that in chocolate), the fat in one's body will look exactly like chocolate fat. If, on the other hand, one eats a lot of cheese, the fat in one's body will look exactly like the fat in cheese.

In a British study, scientists isolated a number of people in a room for a week, allowing them to eat low-fat or fat-free CHO to their hearts' content. After a week, these people had only gained a maximum of 1,5 kg. When these same people were isolated and allowed to eat high-fat foods to their hearts' desire, some of them picked up as much as 7 kg! This shows clearly that in order to lose weight (or rather fat), one needs to cut down on one's intake of visible and hidden fats. All the recipes in this book are much lower in fat than ordinary recipes and we also show you, in the choice of ingredients and preparation methods, how to decrease the fat content of all meals and snacks. Do not, however, avoid fat altogether. One needs a small quantity of good fats in the diet so that all the essential fatty acids are ingested. These are needed for their favourable effect on blood lipids, the skin and overall health, as well as to prevent cravings due to overly strict dieting.

Eat regular, small meals

Regular, smaller, snack type meals are recommended to lose weight and stay slim. Do not, however, end up eating all the time! Increased insulin secretion is stimulated when large meals are eaten and insulin plays a role in how we store fat. Hyperinsulinaemia (too much insulin) is a major contributor to overweight, high body fat levels and inability to lose weight. To facilitate weight loss and stay slim, it is therefore of the utmost importance that there should be no major increase in insulin secretion. It is also important not to cut food intake too drastically, as any major cut in food intake, especially to levels below 4 200 kJ per day, usually leads to a slowing down of the metabolism. Less is not always best!

Eat lower GI foods

Another important aspect of weight loss is to keep blood glucose levels as stable as possible, and the best way to do this is to implement the concept of the GI. In a South African study (reported in *The GI Factor*, by Jenny Brand Miller et al.), it was found that people on a low GI slimming diet lost 2 kg more weight over a period of twelve weeks than their counterparts on a high GI diet. What was astounding was that both groups were given the exact same quantity of fat, kJ, protein, CHO and fibre. The success of the low GI slimming diet was attributed to the fact that a low GI diet does not cause a major insulin response, resulting in lower insulin levels and more stable blood glucose levels. This, in turn, assists the body in losing body fat, which is prevented by high insulin levels. In addition, low GI CHO also help to keep you feeling satisfied for longer, and to prevent 'sweet cravings'.

Exercise regularly

Regular exercise is an essential part of health and especially of successful weight management. It is, in fact, so important that the SA Dietary Guidelines (page 14) place exercise second on the list, even though it is not, strictly speaking, a dietary guideline! Exercise increases lean body mass, which in turn increases the metabolism. Trying to slim without doing regular exercise can lead to muscle loss, because the body finds it easier to convert muscle into energy than to burn body fat for energy, leading to a slowing down of the metabolism. This is especially true if food intake is cut drastically. So, to lose fat most effectively, don't do anything drastic! Forget about dieting and just eat ordinary lower fat, lower GI meals (except after exercise) and exercise daily. Your eating plan for weight management must be one you can follow for the rest of your life. Do watch the size of your portions;

you won't lose weight if you eat too much, even if you are eating the right foods. To help you, we have included the portion sizes for each recipe. And be patient: it takes time to burn fat!

Find out why you eat

If you eat for emotional, physical or circumstantial reasons, instead of in response to your body's needs (i.e. true hunger), you will have to tackle these reasons, otherwise you will never get rid of excess body weight and maintain your weight. (See *Eat Smart and Stay Slim: the GI Diet*, to find out whether you are a compulsive eater.)

Sports nutrition

The only exception to the low GI guideline applies during and/or after exercise. Generally speaking, to sustain energy, we should all eat low GI carbohydrate (CHO) foods most of the time. Sportsmen and women, however, should only eat low GI CHO one to two hours before exercise, and then only resume low GI eating a couple of hours after completing the exercise, depending on its duration and intensity. It is best to consume high GI CHO foods or drinks immediately after exercise lasting about one hour, and during and immediately after exercise lasting more than one hour, as well as for a few hours after exercise, once again depending on the duration and intensity. Intermediate GI foods and drinks during and/or after exercise are recommended for the sportsman or woman with diabetes, and those who have blood sugar (glucose) sensitivity.

Pre-sport or event

Consume about 1 g low GI CHO per 1 kg body weight, one to two hours before exercise. Low GI foods and drinks release glucose slowly and steadily, so they maintain a healthy 'petrol' level during the activity or sporting event.

During the event

Competitions or training sessions that last for more than 60 to 90 minutes require high GI foods and drinks (intermediate for persons with diabetes) at a rate of 30–60 g CHO per hour, depending on body weight and intensity of exercise. If the duration of the exercise is less than 90 minutes, the low GI food/drink that was taken beforehand should be sufficient to sustain blood glucose at a healthy level and only water need be consumed, at a rate of ±500 ml (±2 c) per hour.

Post-sport or event

It is crucial to consume at least 1 g of high GI (intermediate for persons with diabetes) CHO per 1 kg body weight within the first 30 to 60 minutes of completing exercise, together with some protein. If the exercise lasted longer than 60 to 90 minutes, 1 g high GI CHO per 1 kg body weight should be consumed every two hours. The reason for this is that the exercised muscles continue to absorb glucose from the blood stream and this happens at the fastest rate during the first 30 to 60 minutes after exercise. The replenishment of glycogen into the fatigued muscle is faster if higher GI products are consumed as soon as possible after exercise ends, due to the action of the enzyme glycogen resynthetase. Doing this can prevent severe hypoglycaemia and one should also be ensured of sustained energy levels and replenished glycogen levels in the muscles and liver. Consuming some protein with the CHO directly after exercise will ensure full body muscle recovery.

For very active people, i.e. those who train two to three hours every morning, or an hour every morning and an hour every evening, it may mean having to eat intermediate to high GI foods most of the time. If, however, training is scaled down before an event, low GI CHO should dominate all meals for the best **carbo-loading** effect. **Carbo-loading** can enhance performance in some people, but not in all. It is a good idea to try out any dietary changes long before the event to prevent any gastro-intestinal discomfort that may result from the higher CHO diet during the last three days prior to competing, for example, eating low GI cereals, bread (with jam), fruit and fruit juices for breakfast, and substituting pasta (macaroni, spaghetti, etc.) for some of your meat at suppertime, but still including lots of vegetables.

How sportsmen should use this recipe book

The recipes in this book are all lower GI and suitable for daily consumption. Those suitable for carbo-loading before a sports event are clearly marked in the dieticians' notes provided with each recipe. Sportsmen and women who need high GI meals after their sports activity, can substitute a high GI CHO for a low GI CHO in most of the recipes in this book; this will convert the meal into a low-fat, higher GI meal. For example, higher GI rice or high GI potatoes may be used instead of lower GI rice. Sportsmen should still eat low-fat meals, but high GI CHO foods are required during and for a few hours after exercise, depending on its duration and intensity.

The vegetarian diet

Last, but not least, this recipe book is also suitable for vegetarians. All the recipes – except for a few main courses and light meals that contain meat, fish and chicken – are suitable, and many of these meals can be turned into vegetarian dishes simply by replacing the meat, fish or chicken with one or two tins of beans [one tin of cooked dry beans is equivalent to 250 ml (1 c) home-cooked dry beans]. One section of main courses contains recipes that do not call for meat, fish or chicken. These recipes teach the inexperienced vegetarian how to incorporate beans and legumes into meals in a tasty way, without the beans dominating the entire meal, and ensuring at the same time that the meals are nutritionally balanced.

Many vegetarians are not sure how and what to eat. These recipes teach vegetarians how to make vegetarian meals that do not compromise good nutrition. Please note that a large percentage of the vegetarian dishes in most recipe books are high in fat. We had to limit the quantity of cheese and other sources of hidden fat in these recipes to ensure that every recipe complied with our lower fat recommendations.

The nutritional analysis of the recipes

You will notice that each recipe is accompanied by a box containing nutritional information. All the values are rounded off to the nearest whole number. Each box contains the following information and reflects the amounts per serving:

GLYCEMIC INDEX (GI) A calculated value. The value in real life will probably be lower, due to the interaction of the different nutrients with each other. The GI gives an indication of how quickly, and by how much, the food will affect blood glucose levels.

CARBOHYDRATE (g) This value gives the total carbohydrate (CHO) content per serving and includes the CHO present in the dairy, starch, vegetables and fruit.

PROTEIN (g) This represents the total amount of protein per serving.

FAT (g) This value reflects the total fat content of the serving per person. Saturated fat and cholesterol values are not given, but they are kept low throughout. The GIFSA logos are a reflection of how well the recipe complies with the low fat and saturated fat requirements as laid out in the GIFSA specifications and those of the Heart Foundation (see below).

FIBRE (g) The total quantity of fibre per serving, including soluble and insoluble fibre.

KILOJOULES (kJ) The total number of kilojoules (energy) per serving. To obtain calorie values, simply divide by 4.2.

GLYCEMIC LOAD (GL) Reflects the 'oomph' or impact one serving of the dish will have on blood glucose levels, taking the amount of CHO and GI into consideration. One serving of the recipes with a GL below 10 will have a minimal impact on blood glucose levels, even if the GI of the dish is intermediate or high. Recipes with higher GL values must be eaten in the recommended portion size to prevent a huge impact on blood glucose levels. The GL is a reflection of the GI, linked to the portion size of CHO; the larger the portion, the higher the GL.

SODIUM – although we have not indicated the sodium content per serving, we did include it in our analysis, to make sure that all the recipes have a sodium content of less than 400 mg per serving; in fact, most of them are below 300 mg.

For each recipe, the portions of different food groups per serving are given.

For example: One serving is equivalent to 1 starch + 1 protein. (Consult a dietician if you want to know how many portions of starch, protein, fat, etc., you should consume per day, as this varies according to your weight, gender, activity, etc. See www.gifoundation.com or www.dietetics.co.za.

The nutritional contents of one portion for each food group is as follows:

- DAIRY The analysis for a low-fat dairy portion applies: 523 kJ, 8 g protein, 5 g fat and 12 g CHO.
  Where applicable, the analysis of a fat-free dairy portion was used: 340 kJ, 8 g protein, 0 g fat and 12 g CHO.
- PROTEIN The analysis for a medium-fat protein portion applies: 328 kJ, 7 g protein and 5.5 g fat.
- LEAN PROTEIN The analysis for a low-fat protein portion applies: 233 kJ, 7 g protein and 3 g fat.
- STARCH A starch portion implies the following: 289 kJ, 15 g CHO, 2 g protein and traces of fat.
- FAT A fat portion implies the following: 190 kJ and 5 g fat.
- VEGETABLES The kJ and CHO allocation per vegetable portion is: 119 kJ, 5 g CHO and 2 g protein.
  When the kJ allocated to the other food group portions in a recipe used up all the kJ, we did not count the kJ of the vegetables, even if the recipe contained some.
- FRUIT A fruit portion implies the following: 255 kJ and 15 g CHO.

MEASURES USED

In all the recipes in this book, the following measures (abbreviations in brackets) were used.

We used metric measuring spoons, measuring cups and measuring jugs.

1/4 teaspoon (t) = 1 ml	1/3 cup (c) = 80 ml
1/2 teaspoon (t) = 2-3 ml	2/5 cup (c) = 100 ml
1 teaspoon (t) = 5 ml	1/2 cup (c) = 125 ml
2 teaspoons (t) = 10 ml	3/5 cup (c) = 150 ml
1/2 tablespoon (T) = 7 ml	3/4 cup (c) = 180 ml
1 tablespoon (T) = 15 ml	4/5 cup (c) = 200 ml
2 tablespoons (T) = 30 ml	1 cup (c) = 250 ml
1/5 cup (c) = 50 ml	2 cups (c) = 500 ml
1/4 cup (c) = 60 ml	

GIFSA's lower fat, GI rated choice

The GIFSA lower fat, GI rated choice is a range of logos that indicate that these products are low(er) in fat, saturated fat, trans-fatty acids and cholesterol; have a GI rating; allow a minimum of sodium and caffeine; and also have fibre specifications. These ratings are offered in some restaurants and takeaway shops in South Africa as a separate, lower GI, lower fat menu, and the GIFSA logo appears on some products in supermarkets. Listed below are the logos for the different ratings, with explanations. Please refer to www.gifoundation.com for a glossary of relevant terms.

All the recipes in this book are lower in fat and have a lower GI value than regular recipes. The reason some recipes have an intermediate GI is due to the fact that they contain flour (and not necessarily due to their sugar content). All recipes, however, have a GI value of 62 or below, which the World Health Organisation (WHO) regards as 'safe' for all persons with diabetes. The recipes in this book are endorsed by GIFSA, as indicated by the logo which is their official endorsement mark.

The comprehensive *South African Glycemic Index & Load Guide* is available from the GI Foundation of SA (GIFSA) at www.gifoundation.com. It lists the GI of most commonly eaten foods in South Africa, as well as the GL, CHO, protein, fat, fibre and kJ content per portion. It also gives a comprehensive explanation of the GI and GL and how to practise food combining.

Also please note that there is a Recommended Food/ Product List at the end of the book (page 120), containing a list of lower fat, lower GI products available in SA.

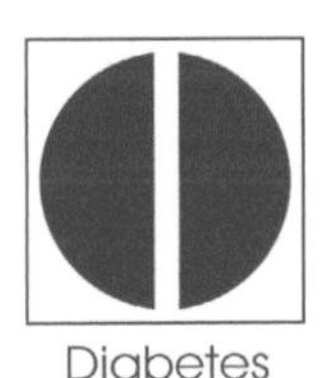

The Diabetes South Africa (DSA) logo is also GI, fat, sodium and caffeine controlled and is used to indicate that the product is suitable for persons with diabetes.

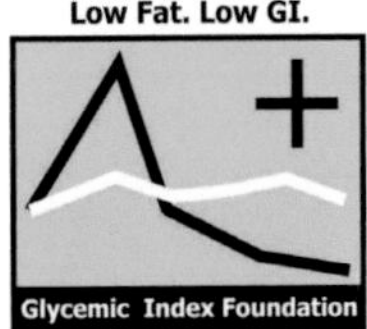	**GIFSA Green plus + logo implies that the product:** • Can be eaten frequently • Is truly low in total fat (≤3 g fat/100 g food), low in saturated fat, trans-fatty acids and cholesterol • Has a very low GI (≤40) • Has a low sodium and caffeine content • Has a high fibre content, where applicable
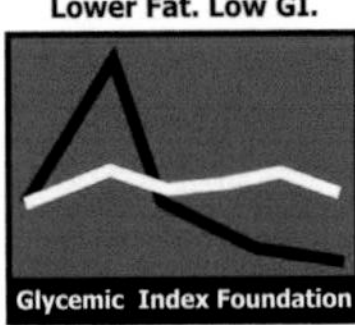	**GIFSA Green logo implies that the product:** • Can be eaten often, i.e. most of the time • Is lower in total fat (≤10 g fat/100 g food), saturated fat, trans-fatty acids and cholesterol than its regular counterpart • Has a low GI (≤55) • Has a low sodium and caffeine content • Has a moderate fibre content, where applicable
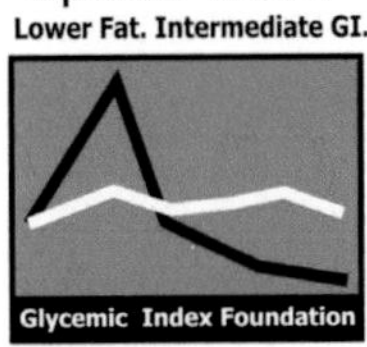	**GIFSA Orange logo implies that the product:** • Should be kept for 'special treats' (People who have diabetes should preferably reserve it for after exercise lasting one hour, or during and after exercise lasting more than one hour) • May be slightly higher in total fat, saturated fat, trans-fatty acids and cholesterol, but still much lower in fat than its regular counterpart, i.e. it contains ≤15 g fat/100 g food • Has an intermediate GI (56–69 GI) (some of these products could have a low GI, but fall into this group due to a slightly higher fat content) • Has a moderately low sodium and caffeine content
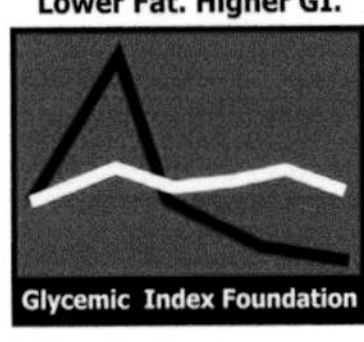	**GIFSA Red logo implies that the product:** • Is best for regular sportsmen and women after exercise lasting one hour and during and after exercise lasting more than one hour • Is low/moderate in fat, saturated fat, trans-fatty acids and cholesterol, but still much lower in fat than its regular counterpart, i.e. it contains ≤15 g fat/100 g food • Has a high GI (70+) • Has a moderately low sodium and caffeine content

Shortened Glycemic Index list of South African lower fat foods

(The GI Value of Glucose = 100)

Foods are listed in food groups, and in order of GI, starting with the lowest GI

Low GI list (GI ≤55) – Ideal before exercise and when inactive, i.e. most of the time						
Dairy	Cereals and porridges	Starches	Fruit	Vegetables	Sugars and snacks	Drinks
Milk Low-fat or fat-free milk (plain and flavoured) Buttermilk, low-fat **Yoghurt** Low-fat and fat-free (plain and sweetened) **Custard** Low-fat or fat-free custard (unsweetened and sweetened – cooled down) **Ice cream** Low-fat (sweetened and unsweetened)	**Cereals** Kellogg's All-Bran Hi-Fibre Bokomo Fibre Plus ProNutro whole-wheat (Original and Apple Bake) ProNutro Original with low-fat milk Spar Bran Flakes Bokomo Bran Flakes Kellogg's All-Bran Fruitful Kellogg's All-Bran Flakes with milk **Muesli** Fine Form Muesli Morning Harvest Muesli (Bokomo) Nature's Source Mueslis: Mixed Berries, Orange & spices, Apple & cinnamon **Porridge** Cold mealie meal SPP Insta-Meal Soya Life Porridge Oat bran, uncooked Oats-so-easy, Natural **Breads and Crackers** **Breads** Dense, heavy loaves Fine Form multigrain brown bread Nature's Harvest brown seed loaf Uncle Salie's homemade brown seed loaf Duens seed loaf Pumpernickel Sourdough bread Astoria Fruit & Honey, Sunflower seed & Volkorn rye bread Fruit bread, e.g. raisin/banana **Crackers** Provita (Original and Multigrain)	**Pasta** Fine Form pasta All pasta made from durum wheat or durum semolina **Legumes** Dry beans, peas and lentils, cooked or canned Baked beans **Rice** Tastic White Rice Tastic Brown Rice Wild Rice Pearled barley, whole and cracked Pearled wheat (stampkoring), cooked Sushi Bulgur Buckwheat Whole corn (canned and frozen) Corn on the cob Sweetcorn Cold samp Cold mealie rice Cold mealie meal Sweet potato	**Deciduous fruit and berries** e.g. pears, peaches, plums, apples, strawberries, fresh cherries, etc. **Citrus fruit** e.g. oranges, naartjies, grapefruit, and lemons **Other** Grapes (watch portion size) and kiwi fruit **Canned fruit** All of the above in fruit juice Pie apples **Fruit bars** TruFruit dried fruit bars Safari Just Fruit Bars **Fruit Juices** Watch portion sizes! Only 125 ml at a time Apple juice and Appletiser Fresh orange juice Tangerine Teaser, Mango/Orange, Peach/Orange (Liquifruit) Apple, Berry, Melon (Aquabrosia) Grapetiser (white and red)	Most cooked and raw vegetables (except those that are intermediate or high GI)	**Sugars** Fructose, not more than 20 g per day Inulin / FOS Lactitol Maltitol Sorbitol Xylitol Mannitol Lactose Polydextrose 'Sugalite' **Snacks** Home-made low-fat popcorn; 'Just Popcorn' Instant pudding made with low-fat milk Quickie, low GI snack bar 'Lean Buns' Fine Form Green Fig Bar Jepsa low GI rusks Carob (chocolate substitute) **Jams** Fine Form jam Rhodes fruit spreads Naturlite fruit spreads	Ice tea lite Mineral water lite Biozest Vitrace Milo Glucema SR Ensure Sustagen Up & Go Nutren Diabetes/Fibre Soya Life Drink SPP Insta-drink Mageu Number 1 Get-on-up Mnandi Amahewu

For a comprehensive GI and GL list of most foods eaten in South Africa, see *The South African Glycemic Index and Load Guide* by Gabi Steenkamp and Liesbet Delport (GIFSA), available from www.gabisteenkamp.co.za or www.gifoundation.com or most bookstores. Consult your local dietician for help in implementing the Glycemic Index (GI) and Glycemic Load (GL).

Intermediate GI list (GI 56–69)

Ideal for persons with diabetes and those with sensitive blood sugar after exercise lasting one hour and during and after exercise lasting longer than one hour

Dairy	Cereals and porridges	Starches	Fruit	Vegetables	Sugars and Snacks	Drinks
Condensed milk Mega Lite	PORRIDGE (GI lower when cooked with milk) Oats (cooked and raw): Bokomo, Pick 'n Pay No Name, Spar, Woolworths Mealie meal, reheated or with added corn Jungle Oats, cooked CEREALS (GI lower when eaten with milk) Bokomo ProNutro Flakes Bokomo Maximise Kellogg's All-Bran Flakes Shredded Wheat Kellogg's Coco Pops Crunchers Kellogg's Corn Pops Kellogg's Hunny B's Kellogg's Frosties Kellogg's Strawberry Pops Kellogg's All-Bran Honey Nut Crunch	Baby/new potatoes Basmati rice Couscous Mealie meal porridge – reheated or with added corn Samp and beans Sweetcorn, creamstyle, canned 'Sticky' rice (arborio rice) Breads and crackers BREADS Astoria wheat-free pumpkin seed rye, linseed rye, pecan nut rye Mustard and plain rye bread Pita bread Woolworths fruit and seed loaf Woolworths seed loaf CRACKERS Provita (Oats and Brown Sugar) Ryvita Crackermate Lites (Sesame and Wholewheat)	TROPICAL FRUIT e.g. banana, mango, pawpaw, pineapple, litchi, guava, melon DRIED FRUIT sultanas, dates, raisins,currants and cake mix CANNED FRUIT all above fruits canned in syrup FRUIT JUICES most fruit juices, except those listed as high or low GI; only 125 ml at a time	Beetroot Carrots Marogo Spinach	SUGARS Sugar/sucrose SNACKS Ouma Nutri Rusks Homewheat Digestive Biscuits (Bettasnack) Provita Bites (Cocoa, Oats & Brown sugar) Quickbreak Bran & Raisin Bar (Bokomo) JAMS Jam, homemade Raw honey Jelly	Regular cold drinks – cordials and soft drinks, ice tea, fruit juice Only 125 ml at a time

High GI list (GI 70 +)

Ideal after exercise lasting one hour or during and after exercise lasting longer than one hour (healthy sportsmen and women)

Dairy	Cereals and porridges	Starches	Fruit	Vegetables	Sugars and Snacks	Drinks
None	CEREALS (GI lower when eaten with milk) Weetbix (regular and sugar free) All-Bran Toasted Muesli (Kellogg's) Puffed Wheat Caramel Coco Pops Crunchy Nut Cornflakes Nutrific Rice Krispies Coco Pops Cornflakes Froot Loops (Kellogg's) Special K (Kellogg's) Flavoured ProNutro PORRIDGE (GI lower when cooked with milk) Instant Oats, flavoured Jungle oats (raw) & Tiger Oats Morvite Maltabella Mealie meal – refined and coarse Polenta	Mealie rice Minute noodles Pasta made from flour Samp, polenta 'Regular' potatoes, boiled, mashed, baked, fried, chips Cornflour Rice flour Potato flour Gravy powder Soup powder Breads and Crackers BREAD All brown, white and ordinary whole-wheat bread, all bread rolls and anything made from cake flour, bread flour and whole-wheat flour CRACKERS Rice cakes and corn thins Snackbread, white and wholewheat Cream crackers	Dried fruit rolls Watermelon FRUIT JUICES Ceres Medley of Fruits Ceres Litchi	Green beans and potato Hubbard squash Pumpkin Turnips Parsnips Note: Although some vegetables have an intermediate or high GI, it is not a reason to exclude them from your diet, as most people don't eat large enough portions for the higher GI to have a negative effect on blood glucose levels (vegetables have a low GL).	SUGARS Glucose Dextrose Maltose Maltodextrin JAMS Commercial honey Watermelon pieces SNACKS Sweets – boiled and jelly type Marie biscuits Boudoir biscuits Cakes (regular) Muffins (regular) Scones Tapioca (boiled with milk) Tofu (frozen dairy-free dessert)	Energade Game Lucozade Powerade

Bran and oat loaf

Cuts into 18 slices

10 ml (2 t) instant yeast
400 ml ($1^3/_5$ c) warm water
15 ml (3 t) sugar
500 ml (2 c) lower GI oats
625 ml ($2^1/_2$ c) Nutty Wheat flour, sifted
250 ml (1 c) oat bran, pressed down
250 ml (1 c) Hi Fibre Bran cereal
2.5 ml ($^1/_2$ t) salt
1 apple, grated *do not leave out*
30 ml (2 T) canola or olive oil

1. Place the instant yeast in a cup with 60 ml ($^1/_4$ c) of the warm water and 5 ml (1t) of the sugar. Stir to dissolve all the yeast and set aside, so the yeast can be activated.
2. Place all the dry ingredients, including the bran sifted out from the Nutty Wheat flour, and the grated apple in a large bowl and mix well.
3. Make two wells in the dry ingredients and pour half the water into each well.
4. To one well add the oil and, once you have checked that the yeast is active (foaming), pour the yeast into the other well of water.
5. Mix well, but not for too long, with a wooden spoon – this will be difficult as it forms a very stiff mixture.
6. Spoon the stiff dough into a greased loaf tin.
7. Sprinkle with oats and then use your hands to flatten the bread and spread the oats evenly.
8. Leave in a warm spot to prove for 30 minutes.
9. Bake at 180 °C for 60 minutes, or until the bread starts to come away from the edge of the loaf pan.

This makes a very dense, moist and heavy bread that is excellent with soup or used for coffee shop type open sandwiches.
It is not suitable for packed lunch type sandwiches.
Sliced, this bread freezes well.

Dieticians' notes

- This bread is very high in fibre and is hence a very dense, heavy bread. It is more like the German breads than our standard sponge-like breads. Good for **carbo-loading**.
- One slice of this bread topped with low fat cheese, ham or other lean cold meats makes an ideal slimmer's breakfast.
- Remember 1 slice is equivalent to 2 starches, thus only 1 slice should be eaten at a meal as the only portion of (low GI) starch.

Nutrients per slice

GI intermediate (60) • Fat 4 g Carbohydrate 26 g • Fibre 5 g • Protein 5 g • kJ 668

ONE SLICE IS EQUIVALENT TO 2 STARCH
GL 15

Fruit and nut muesli

Makes 500 g (10 x 50 g servings)

625 ml ($2^1/_2$ c) lower GI oats
315 ml ($1^1/_2$ c) All-Bran Flakes
250 ml (1 c) Hi-Fibre Bran cereal
22 ml ($1^1/_2$ T) raisins
45 ml (3 T) sultanas
60 ml (4 T) dried peach, pear, apple, apricot, chopped
45 ml (3 T) mixed nuts, chopped

1. Mix all the ingredients together.
2. Store in an airtight container.
3. Serve with 250 ml (1 c) low-fat or skim milk, and/or yoghurt

Dieticians' notes

- When eaten with milk, the GI of the meal is lowered slightly to below 55.
- This muesli is suitable for **carbo-loading** as it has a high long-acting carbohydrate content with not too much fat or protein.
- For **spastic colon sufferers**, remember to omit the raisins and sultanas, and to chop the nuts very finely. (Simply add more of the chopped fruit to make up for the raisins.)
- A 50 g serving is $^1/_2$ cup or 4 heaped tablespoons.

Nutrients per serving

GI intermediate (58) • Fat 4 g Carbohydrate 28 g • Fibre 7 g • Protein 5 g • kJ 736

ONE 50 G SERVING IS EQUIVALENT TO $1^1/_2$ STARCH AND 1 FAT
GL 16

Trail muesli

Makes 500 g (10 x 50 g servings)

500 ml (2 c) lower GI oats
250 ml (1 c) whole-wheat ProNutro
60 ml (1/4 c) Hi Fibre Bran cereal
45 ml (3 T) sultanas
60 ml (1/4 c) dried pears, peaches, apricots or apple, chopped
80 ml (1/3 c) mixed nuts, chopped roughly
60 ml (1/4 c) skim milk powder
125 ml (1/2 c) brown sugar

Nutrients per serving

GI low (55) • Fat 5 g • Carbohydrate 28 g • Fibre 6 g • Protein 5 g • kJ 778

One 50 g serving is equivalent to just under 2 starch and 1 fat
GL 15

1 Mix all the ingredients together.
2 Store in an airtight container.
3 Serve with low-fat milk, or water.

Dieticians' notes

- This muesli was especially formulated to be eaten with water to make it more convenient for **hikers, campers and travellers**.
- It is suitable for those with **diabetes** and for **slimmers**; served either with water or with low-fat milk, or low-fat yoghurt.
- With water the GI is 55.
- With low-fat milk the GI is lowered.
- This muesli is also suitable for **carbo-loading** as it contains a good proportion of low-GI carbohydrate and not too much protein and fat. For carbo-loading purposes it is best eaten with water.
- A 50 g serving is 1/2 cup or 4 heaped tablespoons.

Griddle cakes

Makes 10 griddle cakes

125 ml (1/2 c) flour, sifted before measuring
15 ml (1 T) baking powder
2.5 ml (1/2 t) salt
2 eggs
250 ml (1 c) leftover cooked oats porridge
100 ml (2/5 c) oat bran
5 ml (1 t) canola or olive oil
250 ml (1 c) low-fat milk

Nutrients per griddle cake

GI intermediate (59) • Fat 2 g Carbohydrate 10 g • Fibre 1 g • Protein 4 g • kJ 355

One griddle cake is equivalent to 1 starch and 1/2 fat
GL 6

1 Sift flour, baking powder and salt together.
2 Beat the eggs.
3 Add eggs, oats porridge, oat bran and oil to the flour mixture, and beat until fluffy, but for no longer than 1–2 minutes, as the GI is raised by beating. Add enough milk to give a dropping consistency to the batter.
4 Bake tablespoonsful in a hot non-stick pan, or in a frying pan that has been lightly sprayed with cooking spray.
5 Serve with low-fat grated cheese, a poached egg, Bovril or Marmite, apricot jam or marmalade. Do not spread with margarine or butter. Simply add the topping.

Dieticians' notes

- The toppings are not included in the nutritional analysis.
- Two low-GI ingredients (oats porridge and oat bran) have been added to the batter of these griddle cakes and the GI is still not below 55. This is because of the flour.
- **As soon as flour is part of a recipe, the GI goes up**.
- If the flour is sifted before measuring, the danger of using too much is reduced.

Special crumpets

Makes about 20 crumpets (6 cm diameter)

1 egg, lightly beaten
10 ml (2 t) sugar
2 ml (1/2 t) salt
250 ml (1 c) low-fat or fat-free milk
5 ml (1 t) canola or sunflower oil
250 ml (1 c) cake flour, sifted before measuring
5 ml (1 t) bicarbonate of soda
5 ml (1 t) baking powder
125 ml (1/2 c) oat bran
1 large apple, grated with the skin

Nutrients per crumpet

GI intermediate (60) • Fat 1 g • Carbohydrate 8 g • Fibre 0.6 g • Protein 2 g • kJ 205

ONE CRUMPET IS EQUIVALENT TO 1/2 STARCH
GL 5

1. Beat the egg with a hand whisk in a mixing bowl.
2. Add the sugar and salt and beat for not more than 1 minute.
3. Add half the milk and the oil. Beat for not more than 1 minute.
4. Sift together the flour, bicarbonate and baking powder and stir gradually into the egg and milk mixture with a wooden spoon until smooth and lump free. Do not overmix.
5. Add the rest of the milk, the oat bran and the grated apple and mix gently. Leave the batter to stand for 10 minutes to moisten all the ingredients.
6. Heat a non-stick frying pan and spray with cooking spray. Ladle about 4 separate tablespoons (4 x 15 ml) batter into the pan and cook the four crumpets over moderate to high heat until bubbly on top and light brown underneath. Turn to brown on other side. Repeat with the remaining batter.

Dieticians' notes

- There is no need to spread these crumpets with margarine or butter. Eat dry with a little marmalade or apricot jam and low-fat cheese, if desired.
- Be careful not to beat this batter too much. Beating improves digestibility and thus would increase the GI of the crumpets.
- **It is very important to add the apple**, as this is the vital GI lowering ingredient.

Healthy oat bread

Cuts into 14 slices

150 ml (3/5 c) lower GI oats
250 ml (1 c) oat bran
375 ml (1 1/2 c) flour, sifted before measuring
250 ml (1 c) whole-wheat ProNutro
5 ml (1 t) salt
20 ml (4 t) baking powder
20 ml (4 t) sugar
1 egg
200 ml (4/5 c) low-fat milk
20 ml (4 t) water

1. In a large bowl, mix the oats, oat bran, flour, ProNutro, salt, baking powder, and sugar.
2. Beat egg, milk and water together for not longer than 1 minute.
3. Combine the egg mixture with the flour mixture and stir until dry ingredients are just moistened.
4. Work the dough into a soft ball with your hands, using more oats to prevent it from sticking to your hands. Cover the ball of dough with oats and form into a round loaf shape. Place on a baking sheet and bake for about 1 hour at 180 °C.

To check if the loaf is done, tap the bread with your knuckle.
If it sounds hollow, it is baked through and ready to take out of the oven.
A very easy bread to enjoy at a braai or with soup.
This bread freezes well, whole or sliced. Each slice can be thawed in a toaster as and when required.

Dieticians' notes

- The flour, having a high GI, has to be substituted by the lower GI oats, oat bran and whole-wheat ProNutro. This results in a heavier, yet very tasty bread. However, it must be eaten fresh.
- An excellent bread for **lowering cholesterol** because it has a high oats and oat bran content.
- Remember that 1 slice is equivalent to 1 1/2 starches. Topped with lean protein (boiled egg, ham or fish) it makes a healthy breakfast or lunch – even for **slimmers**. Adding a mixed salad completes the meal.

Nutrients per slice

GI intermediate (61) • Fat 2 g Carbohydrate 20 g • Fibre 3 g • Protein 5 g • kJ 515

ONE SLICE OF BREAD IS EQUIVALENT TO 1 1/2 STARCH
GL 12

Breakfast oats baps

Makes 15 flat soft rolls

500 ml (2 c) lower GI oats
375 ml (1 1/2 c) low-fat milk, warmed
10 ml (2 t) instant dry yeast
30 ml (2 T) sugar
60 ml (1/4 c) warm water
45 ml (3 T) 'lite' margarine, melted
5 ml (1 t) salt
375 ml (1 1/2 c) cake flour, sifted before measuring
125 ml (1/2 c) whole-wheat ProNutro

1. Place the oats in a glass bowl, add warm milk and leave to soak for 30 minutes.
2. Dissolve yeast and 10 ml (2 t) of the sugar in 60 ml (1/4 c) warm water and leave until frothy.
3. To the oats mixture, add the yeast mixture, rest of the sugar, margarine, salt, flour and ProNutro. Stir to form a very stiff dough. Add warm water, if necessary, but not more than 60 ml (1/4 c).
4. On a floured surface knead the dough into a soft ball, using more oats to prevent the dough from sticking to your hands. Place the dough in a mixing bowl, cover with cling wrap, and leave to rise for 1 hour, or prove in the microwave oven (see below) until doubled in volume.
5. Knock back by kneading, then shape into 15 rolls. Place on an ungreased baking tray, cover with a damp, clean cloth and leave in a warm place, or an oven at 50–60 °C, until doubled in size.
6. Dust with flour and bake at 220 °C for about 25 minutes.
7. Eat fresh, or freeze and heat in the oven at 120 °C to thaw.

When working with yeast, it is important that all the ingredients are warm.
To prove yeast dough in the microwave: Place the dough in a glass or ceramic mixing bowl and cover with cling wrap. Microwave on high for 20 seconds, and repeat every 15 minutes until the dough has doubled in size (about 1 hour). Leave the dough in the microwave during this time.

Nutrients per roll

GI Intermediate (62) • Fat 3 g • Carbohydrate 20 g • Fibre 2 g • Protein 4 g • kJ 546

ONE BAP IS EQUIVALENT TO 1 1/2 STARCH AND 1/2 FAT
GL 12

Dieticians' notes

- To lower the GI, we had to substitute at least half of the flour with lower-GI oats and whole-wheat ProNutro. This results in denser rolls that are not as well risen; in fact, they are more like baps. But they are very tasty and well worth the effort as their GI is substantially lower than bought rolls. For hamburger buns, make them a little bigger.
- One bap, filled with lean protein and served with a vegetable soup or salad, makes a balanced meal.

Tropical fruit muesli

Makes 500 g (10 x 50 g servings)

625 ml (2 1/2 c) lower GI oats
250 ml (1 c) Hi-Fibre Bran cereal
250 ml (1 c) All-Bran Flakes
30 ml (2 T) raisins
250 ml dried fruit flakes
75 ml (5 T) sultanas
60 ml (1/4 c) chopped dried apple

1. Mix all the ingredients.
2. Store in an airtight container.
3. Serve with low-fat milk or yoghurt

We found it much easier to make double or treble the recipe at one time as the muesli keeps very well.

Nutrients per serving

GI intermediate (59) • Fat 3 g • Carbohydrate 30 g • Fibre 9 g • Protein 5 g • kJ 733

ONE 50 G SERVING IS EQUIVALENT TO 2 STARCH AND 1/2 FAT
GL 17

Dieticians' notes

- When eaten with milk the GI of this muesli breakfast dish is lowered to less than 55.
- This muesli is suitable for **carbo-loading** as it has a good low-GI carbohydrate content with little fat and protein.
- This is the best option for **slimmers** as it only contains the tiny bit of fat found in wholegrain cereals. Serve with skim milk.

Date and oat muffins

Makes 12 muffins

250 ml (1 c) whole-wheat flour
250 ml (1 c) oat bran
10 ml (2 t) baking powder
2 ml (1/2 t) ground cinnamon
1 ml (1/4 t) ground nutmeg
1 ml (1/4 t) ground cloves
45 ml (3 T) 'lite' margarine
1 large apple, peeled and grated
125 ml (1/2 c) chopped dates
150 ml (3/5 c) skim milk
15 ml (1 T) brown sugar
2 egg whites, whisked to soft-peak stage

Nutrients per muffin

GI intermediate (60) • Fat 3 g • Carbohydrate 20 g • Fibre 3 g • Protein 4 g • kJ 524

ONE MUFFIN IS EQUIVALENT TO 1 STARCH, 1 FRUIT, AND 1/2 FAT
GL 12

1. Preheat the oven to 200 °C.
2. Sift the flour and add back the bran. Add the oat bran, baking powder, cinnamon, nutmeg and cloves. Gently mix with a spoon, lifting up the flour mix to incorporate air.
3. Rub in the margarine.
4. Add the apple and dates. Mix well, but for not more than 1 minute.
5. Add the milk and brown sugar, then fold in the stiffly beaten egg whites.
6. Spoon into sprayed muffin pans and bake in the preheated oven for 15–20 minutes.

Dieticians' notes

- Compare this recipe with the Bran Muffins (page 36) where we use a whole cup of sugar. The latter actually has a lower Glycemic Index! We hope this convinces you that sugar is not always the baddie we thought it was in the past.
- To improve the quality of the fat used in these muffins, 30 ml (2 T) olive or canola oil can be used instead of the 'lite' margarine

Whole-wheat oat muffins

Makes 12 muffins

250 ml (1 c) lower GI oats
250 ml (1 c) oat bran
250 ml (1 c) whole-wheat flour
250 ml (1 c) bran (digestive/wheat bran)
60 ml (1/4 c) sugar
2 ml (1/2 t) salt
20 ml (4 t) baking powder
1 large grated apple *do not leave out*
30 ml (2 T) 'lite' margarine
2 eggs, use only 1 of the yolks, but both egg whites
250 ml (1 c) skim milk
125 ml (1/2 c) apricot jam for spreading on the muffins. See *Dieticians' notes*

Nutrients per muffin

GI intermediate (57) • Fat 4 g • Carbohydrate 23 g • Fibre 5 g • Protein 6 g • kJ 649

ONE MUFFIN (NO CHEESE OR JAM) IS EQUIVALENT TO 2 STARCH AND 1/2 FAT
ONE MUFFIN WITH JAM IS EQUIVALENT TO 2 1/2 STARCH AND 2 1/2 FAT

GL (PLAIN MUFFIN) 13. THIS IS RAISED TO 18 WHEN 10 ml (2 t) JAM IS EATEN WITH THE MUFFIN

1. Mix all the dry ingredients with the grated apple. With the spoon, lift the mixture a few times to incorporate air.
2. Rub the margarine into the dry ingredients until the mixture resembles fine breadcrumbs.
3. Beat eggs and milk together and add to the other ingredients to form a soft mixture. Do not overmix.
4. Spoon into a greased muffin pan.
5. Bake at 180 °C for 15 minutes.
6. Serve without margarine or butter. Simply cut each muffin in half and top with 10 ml (2 level t) apricot jam per muffin.

Dieticians' notes

- The analysis is for the muffin without any jam. If we **add the jam**, the GI is lowered to 55! In this case the apricot jam actually lowers the GI because apricots are very slowly absorbed and have a lower GI than flour. However, by adding the jam more carbohydrates are added and so the GL will increase to 18, which is still acceptable for a meal.
- SO . . . sometimes adding jam to a muffin can lower the GI, as it slows down the absorption of the carbohydrates, but the downside is that it increases the GL.
- With the jam, these muffins are good for **carbo-loading**.
- Adding 2 heaped teaspoons grated, low-fat Cheddar cheese (±10 g) per muffin would increase the fat to 6 g per portion, which is still within reasonable limits.
- **Slimmers**, remember that one muffin contains 2 starches, therefore have no more than 1 muffin as the starch portion of a meal. If you would like to eat a muffin between meals, omit the starch at the next meal.

Bran muffins

Makes 24 large muffins or 48 mini muffins
Note: This batter has to stand overnight

2 eggs
250 ml (1 c) soft brown sugar
60 ml (1/4 c) canola oil
250 ml (1 c) oat bran, pressed down into the cup
375 ml (1 1/2 c) flour, sifted before measuring
500 ml (2 c) digestive bran
2 ml (1/2 t) salt
15 ml (1 T) bicarbonate of soda
5 ml (1 t) ground cinnamon
1 large apple, grated
250 ml (1 c) sultanas
500 ml (2 c) low-fat milk
5 ml (1 t) vanilla essence

Nutrients per muffin
GI intermediate (58) • Fat 3 g •
Carbohydrate 22 g • Fibre 3 g • Protein 3 g •
kJ 550

ONE MUFFIN IS EQUIVALENT TO 1 STARCH, 1 FRUIT AND 1/2 FAT
GL 13

1. Beat together eggs, sugar and oil.
2. Add all the dry ingredients, the grated apple and the sultanas.
3. Add the milk and vanilla.
4. Stir until well blended, but do not overmix.
5. Leave overnight in the refrigerator.
6. When ready to bake, stir and drop into muffin pan holes (fill 3/4 full) and bake at 180 °C for 15 minutes.

This mixture can be kept in the refrigerator for up to 30 days. Do not freeze the batter. Baked muffins freeze very well.

Dieticians' notes

- These muffins are deliciously moist and do not need to be spread with margarine or butter.
- Despite all the oat bran and the bran – we have loaded these muffins as much as we could without sacrificing texture – the GI is still 58. This is due to the *flour*, not the sugar. Even if we halve the sugar, the GI only comes down by 1 point!
- If you have a muffin between meals, omit the starch at your next meal.
- Using low-fat plain or fruit yoghurt in place of the milk lowers the GI to 55.

Cheese and herb scones

Makes 12 scones. No need to add butter or other toppings to these scones; eat as is!

250 ml (1 c) self-raising flour, sifted before measuring
7.5 ml (1 1/2 t) baking powder
375 ml (1 1/2 c), oat bran
1 grated apple, unpeeled *do not leave out*
45 ml (3 T) 'lite' margarine
125 ml (1/2 c) low-fat milk
30 ml (2 T) water
60 g (2 matchboxes) low-fat Cheddar or Mozzarella cheese, grated
10 ml (2 t) grated Parmesan cheese
30 ml (2 T) fresh parsley, chopped
30 ml (2 T) fresh basil, chopped, or 5 ml (1 t) dried basil
5 ml (1 t) dried rosemary
30 ml (2 T) chutney, 'lite' or ordinary

Nutrients per scone
GI intermediate (60) • Fat 5 g •
Carbohydrate 16 g • Fibre 2 g • Protein 5 g •
kJ 558

ONE SERVING IS EQUIVALENT TO 1 STARCH, 1/2 PROTEIN AND 1/2 FAT
GL 10

1. Sift the flour and baking powder into a large bowl, stir in the oat bran and grated apple, lifting the mixture a few times with the spoon to incorporate air. Rub in the margarine.
2. Make a well in the centre. Add milk and water. Mix lightly with a knife, adding extra water if necessary, to make a soft dough.
3. Turn the dough out onto a lightly floured board and knead gently, using the fingertips only. Roll out to a rectangle about 1 cm thick. Scatter half the cheese and all the herbs over the entire surface.
4. Beginning from a long side roll up like a swiss roll to make a thick sausage. Cut into 2 cm slices to make little rounds. Place the rounds side by side on a greased baking tray, spread with chutney and then sprinkle with the remaining cheeses.
5. Bake in a preheated oven at 200 °C for 20 minutes or until golden brown. Do not bake too long as they dry out easily.
6. Serve hot or cold.

Dieticians' notes

- These savoury scones also make a delicious light lunch if served with a tossed salad.
- They are also ideal as a tasty snack.
- Despite the substitution of half the flour with the oat bran, the GI is still higher than we aimed for. In real life, however, these scones showed a much slower absorption rate, therefore we feel they are quite safe.

Mock pumpkin soup

Makes 8 starter portions or 5 meal portions

5 ml (1 t) canola or olive oil
1 large onion, peeled and coarsely chopped
3 medium sweet potatoes, peeled and chopped
250 ml (1 c) dry white wine
1 chicken stock cube or 20 ml (4 t) stock powder dissolved in
500 ml (2 c) boiling water
bunch fresh basil or 2.5 ml (1/2 t) dried basil
250 ml (1 c) low-fat milk
1 ml (1/4 t) ground cinnamon
freshly ground black pepper

1. Heat oil in a saucepan, add the onion and cook over medium heat for 5 minutes.
2. Add the sweet potato, wine and stock; simmer, covered, for 20–30 minutes until the sweet potato is soft.
3. Add the basil leaves and purée the soup in a food processor or blender for no longer than 1 minute.
4. Return to the saucepan, add the milk, cinnamon and pepper to taste and reheat.
5. Serve as a starter or light meal.

This soup is a good replacement for the usual high GI pumpkin soup. If serving for starters, use one ladle per portion. For a meal use 2 ladles per portion.

Dieticians' notes

- The nutrient analysis is for a meal portion. All the values are halved for starters.
- Using sweet potato in this recipe not only effectively lowers the GI of the soup, but also gives the soup a delicious flavour.
- This soup is ideal for **carbo-loading** as it contains lots of sustained-release carbohydrate and very little protein and fat.
- For slimmers, this soup makes a meal on its own. Do not add another starch (e.g. bread). A piece of fruit may be eaten as dessert. If you want to add a slice of bread and low-fat cheese, use the starter portion size.

Nutrients per meal serving

GI low (49) • Fat 3 g • Carbohydrate 45 g • Fibre 6 g • Protein 6 g • kJ 1 158

One serving is equivalent to 3 starch, 1/2 protein/dairy/vegetable
GL 22

Tomato and barley soup

Serves 6

5 ml (1 t) canola or olive oil
1 large onion, peeled and finely chopped
2 cloves garlic, crushed or 10 ml (2 t) minced garlic
5 ml (1 t) curry powder
1 chicken stock cube dissolved in
1.5 litres (6 c) boiling water
250 ml (1 c) split lentils or red lentils
125 ml (1/2 c) pearl barley
1 x 410 g tin tomatoes, chopped with the juice
freshly ground black pepper
chopped fresh parsley, to serve

1. Heat the oil in a large saucepan. Add the onion and garlic and stir while cooking gently until just brown.
2. Add curry powder and cook, stirring, for 1 minute.
3. Stir in the water, stock, lentils, barley, tomatoes, and pepper to taste. Bring to boil and simmer for 45 minutes to 1 hour until the lentils and barley are tender.
4. Sprinkle with freshly chopped parsley and serve with Bran and oat loaf (page 26) or Healthy oat bread (page 30), if desired.

A delicious tomato soup with a hint of curry.
A tasty and filling winter soup that is a meal in itself.

Dieticians' notes

- Barley has a low GI, is rich in soluble fibre and is very effective in **binding cholesterol** as well as lowering morning blood glucose readings in those who have **diabetes**.
- This soup has such a low GI that it can be enjoyed with a slice of ordinary bought bread, if desired. Remember to count the extra STARCH if you have the bread.
- **For carbo-loading** use a double portion with 2 slices of bread. This meal would then contribute 86 g carbohydrates.
- The exceptionally low GL of this soup makes it a perfect lunch for slimmers – even with a slice of low GI bread.

Nutrients per serving

GI low (25) • Fat 2 g • Carbohydrate 28 g • Fibre 8 g • Protein 12 g • kJ 833

One serving is equivalent to 1 1/2 starch, 1 protein and vegetable
GL 7

Minestrone

Serves 6

5 ml (1 t) canola or olive oil
2 onions, peeled and chopped
2 cloves garlic, crushed or 10 ml (2 t) minced garlic
2 rashers of lean bacon, fat removed, chopped
1 x 410 g tin small white beans, drained
1 beef stock cube or 20 ml (4 t) stock powder dissolved in
1.5 litres (6 c) water
2 carrots, diced
2 celery stalks, sliced
2 baby marrows, chopped
3 tomatoes, diced
100 g (1 c) small raw durum wheat pasta shapes
30 ml (2 T) chopped parsley
freshly ground black pepper to taste

1. Heat the oil in a large saucepan and add the onion, garlic and bacon. Cook for 5 minutes or until soft.
2. Add the beans, stock cube and water and simmer for 15 minutes.
3. Add the vegetables and simmer for another 30 minutes.
4. Add the pasta and simmer, uncovered, for 10–15 minutes until the pasta is tender. Stir in the parsley and pepper to taste.
5. Serve with a sprinkling of Parmesan cheese, if desired.

Dieticians' notes

- This soup is so low in GI that it can be eaten with ordinary bought bread. For slimmers, remember the bread counts as another starch.
- By leaving out the pasta, the soup will contain 1 protein and vegetable. Add a slice of bread and you have the perfect **slimmers' meal**.
- For **carbo-loading**, have a double portion of soup, with 2 slices of bread. The meal would then contain 80 g carbohydrates.

Nutrients per serving

GI low (35) • Fat 3 g • Carbohydrate 26 g • Fibre 7 g • Protein 8 g • kJ 694

One serving is equivalent to 1 starch, 1 protein, and vegetable
GL 9

Gourmet vegetable soup

Serves 10

5 ml (1 t) canola or olive oil
2 carrots, cut into strips
500 ml (2 c) cabbage, coarsely chopped
2 onions, peeled and chopped
2 leeks, sliced
1 celery stalk, chopped
2 tomatoes, peeled and chopped
1 x 410 g tin brown or sugar beans, drained
1 litre (4 c) water
2 ml (1/2 t) salt
10 ml (2 t) Worcestershire sauce
freshly ground black pepper to taste
10 slices French bread
60 g (2 matchboxes) low-fat Mozzarella cheese, grated

Nutrients per serving

GI low (50) • Fat 2 g • Carbohydrate 16 g • Fibre 5 g • Protein 6 g • kJ 492

One serving is equivalent to 1 starch, 1/2 protein, and vegetable
GL 8

1. For the soup: Heat oil in a large saucepan and add vegetables. Sauté over low heat for 10 minutes, stirring occasionally.
2. Add the beans, 500 ml (2 c) water and flavourings. Simmer for about 30 minutes, or until the vegetables are soft.
3. For the topping: Lightly toast the slices of bread in a toaster.
4. Remove 60 ml (1/4 c) of the vegetables from the soup and mash or process in a food processor for not more than 1 minute.
5. Spread the mashed vegetables on the slices of toasted bread, and sprinkle with grated cheese. Arrange on a baking tray and bake under the grill until golden brown.
6. Mash the remaining vegetables or process in a food processor for not more than 1 minute. Add the remaining water and simmer to a smooth consistency. Serve hot, with the slices of bread floating on top, or served separately.

Dieticians' notes

- This is a delicious hearty meal on its own.
- This soup is ideal for **carbo-loading** as it has a low GI, high carbohydrate content with not too much protein, and is very low in fat as well. A double portion would yield 32 g carbohydrates. If bread is needed with the meal, use a low GI bread, not normal bought bread, because the GI of the soup is already higher due to the French bread topping.

Lentil soup

Serves 10

1 x 410 g tin chickpeas
1 vegetable stock cube or 20 ml (4 t) stock powder, dissolved in
2 litres (8 c) boiling water
1 large onion, peeled and chopped
10 ml (2 t) sugar
1 x 410 g tin chopped tomatoes
2 (80 g) celery stalks and leaves, sliced
1 x 65 g tin tomato paste
salt and freshly ground black pepper to taste
3 ml (1/2 t) ground ginger
5 ml (1 t) ground cinnamon
200 g (1 c) large green or brown lentils soaked in hot water for 1 hour, or 2 x 410 g tins brown or green lentils
20 ml (4 t) lemon juice (juice of 1/2 lemon)
6 baby marrows, sliced (500 g)
100 g (1 c) durum wheat spaghetti, broken into 4 cm pieces
chopped parsley

1. Drain the chickpeas and place in a large saucepan with the stock, water, onion, sugar, tomatoes, celery and tomato paste. Simmer for 20 minutes and then add salt and pepper to taste.
2. Add ginger, cinnamon and lentils and cook for 20 minutes or until lentils are soft.
3. Add the lemon juice, baby marrows and pasta and add more water, if necessary. Cook for 15 minutes. Just before serving, stir in the parsley.

Dieticians' notes

- This is an ideal **carbo-loading** meal if combined with two slices of bread. Soup and two slices of bread would contribute 54 g of carbohydrate.
- The GI of this soup is low enough to allow ordinary bought bread with the soup. Remember to count the extra starch.

Nutrients per serving

GI low (31) • Fat 1 g • Carbohydrate 24 g • Fibre 8 g • Protein 9 g • kJ 679

ONE SERVING IS EQUIVALENT TO 1 STARCH, 1 PROTEIN AND VEGETABLE
GL 7

Creamy chicken and mushroom soup

Serves 4 (large servings)

180 ml (3/4 c) lower GI oats
5 ml (1 t) canola or olive oil
2 medium onions, peeled and diced
1 clove garlic, crushed
60 ml (1/4 c) dry white wine
1 x 380 g tin low-fat evaporated milk
1 chicken stock cube or 20 ml (4 t) stock powder
1 1/2 tins water (630 ml)
2 chicken breasts, cooked and diced (220 g cooked chicken)
250 g mushrooms, sliced (1 punnet)
pinch of marjoram or origanum
few drops of soya sauce

Nutrients per serving

GI low (38) • Fat 9 g • Carbohydrate 33 g • Fibre 3 g • Protein 28 g • kJ 1385

ONE SERVING IS EQUIVALENT TO 1/2 STARCH, 2 PROTEIN, 1 DAIRY AND VEGETABLE
GL 11

1. In a dry saucepan, stir the oats over low heat until browned. Remove from the saucepan and set aside.
2. Heat the oil in the saucepan and sauté the onion and garlic, stirring constantly, until the onion becomes transparent.
3. Stir in the browned oats, wine, milk and stock.
4. Add 1 1/2 tins of water, using the evaporated milk tin, swirling out the milk left over in the tin.
5. Add the chopped chicken and mushrooms and simmer for 5–10 minutes, stirring to prevent the soup from scorching on the bottom of the saucepan.
6. Season to taste with marjoram and soya sauce.
7. Serve with freshly made Breakfast oat baps (page 32), Bran and oat loaf (page 26) or Healthy oat bread (page 30), if desired.

This recipe makes 4 large servings, a serving being a meal in itself. Bread, or rolls, is only required for the very hungry. As a starter it will serve 6.

Dieticians' notes

- The lower fat and high fibre content is exceptional for such a creamy soup.
- This recipe can be used as a sauce for pasta or rice. Simply use less water. Use one small handful pasta or rice per person and serve with lots of vegetables or salad.

Broccoli and mushroom salad with cottage cheese

Serves 6-8

500 g broccoli or cauliflower
salt and freshly ground black pepper
250 g mushrooms, wiped and sliced (one punnet)
4 spring onions, chopped
250 g smooth, fat-free cottage cheese (1 tub)
175 ml plain or flavoured low-fat yoghurt
60 ml (4 T) 'lite' mayonnaise
60 ml (4 T) chopped parsley
10 ml (2 t) honey
1 ml (1/4 t) celery salt
1–2 pickled gherkins, chopped
paprika

Nutrients per serving

GI low (25) • Fat 2 g • Carbohydrate 10 g • Fibre 3 g • Protein 10 g • kJ 434

ONE SERVING IS EQUIVALENT TO 1 DAIRY AND VEGETABLE
GL 2

1. Trim broccoli or cauliflower and slice lengthwise. Poach in a little boiling water until just tender.
2. Drain, chop coarsely and arrange in a large shallow salad bowl or platter. Season and then add the sliced mushrooms.
3. In a separate bowl, mix the spring onions, cottage cheese, yoghurt, mayonnaise, parsley, honey, celery salt and gherkins.
4. Stir until well blended, adding a little skim milk if the dressing is too thick.
5. Pour over the broccoli (or cauliflower) and mushrooms and dust with paprika.
6. Chill until required.
7. Serve at room temperature.

This appetising salad is very low in fat and adds variety to a buffet. Apricot-flavoured yoghurt will add an interesting tang to the dressing.

Dieticians' note

- Broccoli is one of the most vitamin-dense vegetables around. It is full of antioxidants, and fibre as well. We should all try to eat broccoli every day.

Flageolet vinaigrette (white-bean salad)

Serves 4

1 x 410 g tin small white beans
3–4 leeks or an onion, thinly sliced
1/2 green or red pepper, seeded and chopped
1 large stalk table celery, sliced
100 ml (2/5 c) chopped parsley
10 ml (2 t) sugar
2 tomatoes
60 g (2 matchboxes) feta cheese
6–8 black olives

DRESSING

15 ml (1 T) canola or olive oil
1 clove garlic
30 ml (2 T) lemon juice
5 ml (1 t) dried origanum
1/2 vegetable stock cube or 10 ml (2 t) stock powder
125 ml (1/2 c) boiling water

Nutrients per serving

GI low (30) • Fat 7 g • Carbohydrate 17 g • Fibre 8 g • Protein 8 g • kJ 775

ONE SERVING IS EQUIVALENT TO 1 STARCH, 1 PROTEIN AND VEGETABLE
GL 5

1. Make the dressing by mixing all the dressing ingredients.
2. In a glass bowl, microwave the beans for 2 minutes on high.
3. Add the salad dressing to the beans and mix lightly with a fork, taking care not to break up the beans.
4. Add the leeks (or onion), pepper, celery, parsley and sugar to the bean mixture. Mix gently.
5. Cover and chill for at least 2 hours or chill overnight.
6. To serve, adjust seasoning of bean salad with salt and pepper, if needed.
7. Spoon onto a large flat platter. Surround the heap of bean salad with thinly sliced tomatoes and crumble the feta cheese on top of the beans.
8. Place a few olives on the salad to finish it. Serve as a meal.

Dieticians' note

- An unusual, appetising, well-balanced meal on its own. Easy to prepare for those unexpected guests on the weekend.

Quick bean and noodle salad

Serves 6

1 x 410 g tin baked beans in tomato sauce
250 g (2 c) cooked small-shell durum wheat noodles
60 ml (4 T) 'lite' salad cream or 'lite' mayonnaise (low-oil dressing)
60 ml (4 T) 'lite' fruit chutney or ordinary chutney
1/2 small onion, peeled and finely chopped
1/2 green pepper, seeded and finely chopped
3 'lite' viennas, sliced
freshly ground black pepper
lettuce leaves, optional

Nutrients per serving

GI low (38) • Fat 4 g • Carbohydrate 27 g • Fibre 7 g • Protein 9g • kJ 739

One serving is equivalent to 1 1/2 starch and 1 protein
GL 10

1. Mix the beans with the cooked shell noodles.
2. Fold in the mayonnaise and chutney.
3. Add the onion, green pepper and viennas.
4. Season to taste, mix well and chill.
5. Serve on lettuce leaves.

This is a very quick and easy salad to make, and a meal in itself. This salad can be served hot or cold.

Dieticians' notes

- By doubling the quantity of noodles, this salad makes a delicious **carbo-loading** meal that contains 38 g carbohydrate and has a GI of 33.
- It is important to use the lower-fat viennas to keep the fat low.
- Legumes and pasta make a wonderful, low GI combination. Remember this when choosing salads at a salad bar in a restaurant. Avoid the high-fat salad dressings by 'draining' the salad as much as possible.
- This salad, on its own, makes an ideal slimmers' lunch or light supper. Serve with a large mixed salad – or add salad vegetables to the noodle salad.

Green-bean salad

Serves 12

1 x 410 g tin butter beans
1 x 410 g tin green beans
1 x 410 g tin garden peas
1 onion, peeled and finely chopped
2 tomatoes, chopped
1/2 green pepper, finely chopped (optional)
15 ml (1 T) canola or olive oil
30 ml (2 T) lemon juice
10 ml (2 t) sugar
5 ml (1 t) mixed herbs
freshly ground black pepper to taste

Nutrients per serving

GI low (35) • Fat 1 g • Carbohydrate 8 g • Fibre 3 g • Protein 3 g • kJ 277

One serving is equivalent to 2 vegetable
GL 3

1. Drain the beans and peas and mix with the onion, tomatoes and green pepper. Reserve.
2. Mix the remaining ingredients in a shaker.
3. Shake well and pour over the bean and pea mixture.
4. Chill overnight to enhance the flavour.

This salad will keep for up to two weeks in the refrigerator.
It is ideal to make in advance for a braai, picnic, camping and even for self-catering holidays.

Dieticians' notes

- A wonderfully easy, low-fat salad that can be made in advance and served at very short notice.
- Of all the legumes, butter beans are probably the most versatile. They are creamier in texture than other dried beans and have a pleasant nutty flavour. This makes them ideal for adding to all salads, stir-fries, stews, curries and casseroles.

Piquant three-bean salad

Serves 12

1 x 410 g tin butter beans, drained
1 x 410 g tin baked beans in tomato sauce
1 x 410 g tin French-cut green beans, drained, or 250 ml (1 c) cooked fresh green beans
15 ml (1 T) sugar
2 ml (1/2 t) mustard powder
15 ml (1 T) canola or olive oil
60 ml (1/4 c) white or brown vinegar
5 ml (1 t) dried basil
freshly ground black pepper to taste

1. Mix the 3 tins of beans.
2. Heat the sugar, mustard powder, oil, vinegar and basil in a saucepan until the sugar has dissolved. Stir continuously.
3. Pour the sauce over the bean mixture.
4. Season with pepper to taste and mix well.
5. Chill overnight or for at least 3 hours.
6. Serve cold.

This salad will keep for as long as 2 weeks in a sealed container in the refrigerator. It is ideal for making in advance for picnics, camping and even for self-catering holidays.

Nutrients per serving (80 ml/1/3 c)
GI low (44) • Fat 1 g • Carbohydrate 11 g • Fibre 5 g • Protein 4 g • kJ 322

ONE SERVING IS EQUIVALENT TO 1/2 STARCH AND 1 VEGETABLE
GL 5

Dieticians' notes

- Half a portion is equal to 1/2 STARCH.
- This very low-fat salad goes well with all outdoor meals.
- For **diabetic individuals** this low GI salad is ideal to take along to a 'bring-and-braai'.
- Even if the quantity of sugar is doubled, it hardly affects the GI.
- If you have the full portion remember to have less starch (or protein) at the same meal.

Chilled tuna salad

Serves 5

250 ml (1 c) uncooked pearl wheat, or 750 ml (3 c) cooked pearl wheat (stampkoring)
1/2 green pepper, seeded and finely chopped
1/2 onion, peeled and finely chopped
2 x 170 g tins tuna chunks in brine, drained and flaked
10 black olives
3 large tomatoes, diced
125 ml (1/2 c) 'lite' mayonnaise
30 ml (2 T) 'lite' tomato sauce, or ordinary tomato sauce
2 ml (1/2 t) marjoram
30 ml (2 T) chopped parsley
freshly ground black pepper

1. Cook the pearl wheat in lots of water until tender. Drain.
2. Add the green pepper, onion, tuna, olives and tomatoes. Mix gently until combined.
3. Mix mayonnaise and tomato sauce with the marjoram and pour over the salad. Mix the parsley in last.
4. Season to taste with pepper. Chill.
5. Serve on a bed of lettuce with Bran and oat loaf (page 26), Healthy oat bread (page 30) or Breakfast oat baps (page 32).

Nutrients per serving
GI low (33) • Fat 5 g • Carbohydrate 19 g • Fibre 4 g • Protein 18 g • kJ 846

ONE SERVING IS EQUIVALENT TO 1 STARCH AND 2 PROTEIN
GL 6

Dieticians' notes

- Since the tomato sauce is such a minor ingredient, and its GI is low, any type of tomato sauce may be used.
- In summer this salad makes a wonderful lunch. It can easily be made in the morning and then chilled until the children return home from school.
- This is the ideal lunch for **slimmers**. The very low GI ensures good blood glucose levels and prevents that mid-afternoon craving for a snack. No need to add bread. Rather add a tossed salad or mix the salad vegetables into the tuna salad.

Cabbage and apple salad

Serves 4

1 red apple
1 green apple
10–20 ml (2–4 t) lemon juice
500 ml (2 c) cabbage, finely chopped or grated
60 ml (4 T) plain, low-fat yoghurt
125 ml (1/2 c) low-oil salad cream or low-oil mayonnaise
10 ml (2 t) sunflower seeds
4 lettuce leaves

1. Wash the apples, but do not peel them. Slice thinly or cube. Sprinkle with just enough lemon juice to prevent discolouration.
2. Add the apple to the cabbage and mix lightly with a fork.
3. For the dressing, mix the yoghurt, low-oil salad cream and sunflower seeds. Add 5–15 ml (1–3 t) sugar if too tart.
4. Pour the dressing over the cabbage and apple, toss the salad and spoon into a container with a lid. Chill for 2 hours or longer before use.
5. Serve the salad on the lettuce leaves.

Nutrients per serving

GI low (<30) • Fat 4 g • Carbohydrate 11 g • Fibre 2 g • Protein 2 g • kJ 375

ONE SERVING IS EQUIVALENT TO 1 FAT, 1 FRUIT AND 1 VEGETABLE
GL 3

Dieticians' notes

- This is a deliciously different coleslaw, lower in fat than the traditional one.
- This salad can be made the day before, covered and kept in the refrigerator until ready to serve.
- This recipe makes 4 large portions or 6 smaller portions. The analysis is for the 4 large portions.

Baby potato salad

Serves 8

1 kg baby or new potatoes
250 ml (1 c) young green beans, sliced
500 ml (2 c) cherry tomatoes
1/2 English cucumber, quartered and sliced
90 g lower-fat feta cheese, cut into cubes (3 matchboxes)
freshly ground black pepper

DRESSING
15 ml (1 T) canola or olive oil
30 ml (2 T) vinegar
10 ml (2 t) sugar
1 ml (1/4 t) salt
1 clove of garlic, crushed, or 2 ml (1/2 t) dried garlic
5 ml (1 t) prepared mustard
5 ml (1 t) fresh thyme, or 2 ml (1/2 t) dried thyme
20 ml (4 t) freshly chopped parsley

1. Scrub the baby potatoes, but do not peel them.
2. Place in a large saucepan, half-cover with water and boil until cooked, but still firm. Drain and place in a dish to cool.
3. Meanwhile, wash and slice the green beans and boil until just cooked and still crisp. Drain and cool with the potatoes.
4. Add cherry tomatoes, cucumber and feta cheese. Toss lightly.
5. For the dressing: Mix all the ingredients together and pour over the salad ingredients. Mix gently, but thoroughly.
6. Chill in refrigerator for at least 1 hour.
7. Sprinkle with freshly ground black pepper to taste before serving.

This salad is a feast for the eye and the palate!

Nutrients per serving

GI low (52) • Fat 5 g • Carbohydrate 27 g • Fibre 3 g • Protein 5 g • kJ 731

ONE SERVING IS EQUIVALENT TO 2 STARCH AND 1 FAT
GL 14

Dieticians' notes

- Although regular feta cheese is lower in fat (21 g/100 g) than Cheddar cheese (33 g/100 g), the lower-fat feta is still the main fat contributor in this salad. If you wish to lower the fat content, leave out or halve the feta cheese.
- Be generous with the parsley – it is full of antioxidants, which protect us from disease.
- Baby or new potatoes are lower in GI than mature potatoes, as they are firmer and have more skin in relation to the potato and are therefore digested more slowly. Take care not to overcook them.
- For **diabetic individuals** this is the ideal salad for a braai as it contains less fat and has a lower GI than traditional potato salad.
- Slimmers please note: this salad contains 2 starch. Do not add any more starch. Rather add more (salad) vegetables.

Gabi's salad dressing

Makes 600 ml (20 x 30 ml portions)

1 vegetable stock cube or 20 ml (4 t) stock powder
1/2 small onion, peeled and finely chopped
400 ml (1 3/5 c) boiling water
100 ml (2/5 c) balsamic vinegar
1 ml (1/4 t) crushed garlic
35 ml (7 t) sugar
10 ml (2 t) apple cider vinegar
1 ml (1/4 t) salt
60 ml (1/4 c) olive oil

1. Place the crumbled stock cube and onion in a 1 litre (4 c) measuring jug. Pour the boiling water over both and stir until the stock cube is completely dissolved.
2. Add the rest of the ingredients, except the olive oil, and stir well to mix thoroughly. Lastly, add the oil and stir again.
3. Store in a salad dressing bottle. Shake the bottle every time before pouring the dressing over salad.

This dressing can be stored at room temperature for up to two weeks. Do not refrigerate this salad dressing as the oil will solidify and make it difficult to pour. Because of the vinegar, salad dressings are best stored in glass bottles. Vinegar tends to 'dissolve' some plastics, which means the dressing then becomes contaminated with plastic compounds.

Nutrients per serving

GI low (54) • Fat 2 g • Carbohydrate 2 g • Fibre – • Protein – • kJ 136

ONE SERVING IS EQUIVALENT TO 1/2 FAT
GL 1

Dieticians' notes

- The calculated GI of this dressing is rather high, but in practice it is much lower as it is consumed with the very low GI tossed salad, therefore it really does not have much effect.
- Remember, sugar in this recipe is divided into 20 portions, that equals 1 ml (1/4 t) sugar per person. So **diabetic individuals**, don't panic.
- For a fat-free dressing, simply leave out the oil.

Tossed salad or Greek salad

Serves 6

1/2 lettuce
2 tomatoes
1/4 English cucumber
1 carrot
1 avocado
1 apple
lemon juice

1. Wash and break up the lettuce leaves and arrange on a platter.
2. Cut the tomatoes into quarters, and dice the cucumber. Place on top of lettuce.
3. Peel the carrot, then cut into matchsticks. Sprinkle on top of the other vegetables.
4. Peel the avocado, cut it into cubes and spread on top of the other vegetables.
5. Cut the apple into quarters, slice thinly and sprinkle with just enough lemon juice to prevent them turning brown. Add to the salad.
6. Serve with Gabi's salad dressing (see above) on the side.

Nutrients per serving

(without dressing)

Tossed salad
GI low (<25) • Fat 4 g • Carbohydrate 6 g • Fibre 2 g • Protein 1 g • kJ 267

ONE SERVING IS EQUIVALENT TO 1 FAT AND 1 VEGETABLE
GL NEGL.

Greek salad
GI low (<25) • Fat 8 g • Carbohydrate 7 g • Fibre 2 g • Protein 4 g • kJ 480

ONE SERVING IS EQUIVALENT TO 1/2 PROTEIN, 1 FAT AND 1 VEGETABLE
GL NEGL.

Dieticians' notes

- For a **fat-free** salad, omit the avocado in the salad and the oil in the dressing.
- For a **Greek salad**, add 3 matchboxes of low-fat feta cheese, and 12 olives.
- The nutritional information given alongside is for the salad without the dressing.
- **Slimmers**, please note that only 15 g (1/2 matchbox) feta cheese per person is in the Greek salad. Restaurant Greek salads, however, contain much more cheese, so remember to compensate for the extra protein in these salads by eating less protein in the same meal.

Bean frittata

Serves 6

5 ml (1 t) canola or olive oil
125 g (1/2 packet) lean bacon, fat removed, and chopped
1 onion, peeled and chopped
2 ml (1/2 t) crushed garlic
1/2 red pepper, seeded and chopped
1 potato, cooked and diced
1 x 410 g tin baked beans in tomato sauce *Do not leave out!*
6 eggs
30 ml (2 T) water
salt and freshly ground black pepper to taste
parsley to garnish

Nutrients per serving

GI low (40) • Fat 8 g • Carbohydrate 16 g • Fibre 6 g • Protein 13 g • kJ 781

ONE SERVING IS EQUIVALENT TO 1 STARCH AND 1 1/2 PROTEIN
GL 6

1. Heat the oil and a little water in a frying pan and fry the bacon, onion, garlic and red pepper until the onion is transparent. Add the beans and potato.
2. Beat together the eggs and water, and season to taste. Pour into the frying pan on top of the other ingredients and cook for 6–8 minutes. Lift the edge of the egg mixture as it sets to allow the runny egg to flow underneath it so as to cook all the egg into one big 'pancake'.
3. Place under the grill until golden brown on top, or cover with a lid for 3 minutes to cook the top of the frittata.
4. Sprinkle with parsley, cut into wedges and serve hot with Bran and oat loaf (page 26) or Healthy oat bread (page 30).

Dieticians' notes

- Serve this frittata, preceded by fresh fruit salad, for a delicious and balanced breakfast.
- Although potato has a high GI, in this recipe it makes up a small percentage, and is used together with lots of low-GI ingredients, which makes it quite acceptable.
- Serve with fruit or vegetables (not another starch, e.g. bread)

Mexican bean snack

Serves 4

5 ml (1 t) canola or olive oil
1 onion, peeled and finely chopped
1 clove of garlic, crushed
1/2 green pepper, seeded and chopped
1 tomato, chopped
2 'lite' viennas, sliced
1 x 410 g tin baked beans in tomato sauce
freshly ground black pepper to taste
5 ml (1 t) mild chilli or curry powder
100 g lower-fat cheese, grated (1 c grated)
2 slices of hot toast

Nutrients per serving

GI low (49) • Fat 10 g • Carbohydrate 33 g • Fibre 10 g • Protein 17 g • kJ 1 178

ONE SERVING IS EQUIVALENT TO 2 STARCH AND 2 PROTEIN
GL 16

1. Heat the oil and fry the onion, garlic and green pepper until soft. Add the tomato and simmer for another 3–5 minutes.
2. Add the rest of ingredients, except the cheese and toast, and cook for 5 minutes, stirring occasionally. Add 1/3 of the cheese and heat until the cheese has melted.
3. Pile generously onto the dry toast and sprinkle with the rest of the grated cheese. Serve hot, using half a slice of toast per person.

An unusual and quick meal for Sunday nights or unexpected visitors.

Dieticians' notes

- For a balanced meal, serve fruit for dessert.
- Remember that bread, whether white or brown, has a high GI. But in this dish, by combining the bread with baked beans, the GI is lowered substantially.
- It is important to use 'lite' viennas, otherwise the fat content per portion goes up to 14 g.
- If only half the cheese is used, this dish will be extra lean.
- Slimmers' note: no more starch should be added to this dish. Rather add heaps of (salad) vegetables to make a balanced meal.

Hamburger patties with BBQ sauce

Serves 8

PATTIES
1 x 410 g tin brown or sugar beans, drained
15 ml (1 T) vinegar
15 ml (1 T) Worcestershire sauce
2 ml (1/2 t) crushed garlic
200 g lean topside mince
1 medium onion, peeled and chopped
1 stalk celery, chopped
1 slice bread, crumbled (brown or white)
250 ml (1 c) oat bran
5 ml (1 t) instant beef stock powder
freshly ground black pepper
1 egg
5 ml (1 t) canola or olive oil
4–8 hamburger rolls

BBQ SAUCE
1 onion, peeled and chopped
1 large apple, grated finely
1 ml (1/4 t) crushed garlic
5 ml (1 t) canola or olive oil
60 ml (4 T) tomato sauce
1 tomato, chopped finely
125 ml (1/2 c) water
20 ml (4 t) brown sugar
10 ml (2 t) Worcestershire sauce
5 ml (1 t) salt
10 ml (2 t) prepared mustard

1 For the patties, mash together the beans, vinegar, Worcestershire sauce and garlic, or process in a food processor.
2 Add the minced meat, chopped onion and celery, breadcrumbs, oat bran, beef stock powder, pepper and egg, and mix lightly to a firm consistency.
3 Shape into 8 hamburger patties.
4 Lightly grease a frying pan with 5 ml (1 t) oil, ensuring that the oil is evenly spread all over the pan. Use an egg lifter to spread the hot oil in the pan.
5 Fry the patties for 5 minutes on each side.
6 Serve on unbuttered hamburger rolls with tomato, lettuce and BBQ sauce.

BBQ sauce

1 Sauté onion, apple and garlic in the oil until transparent.
2 Add the rest of the ingredients and simmer for 5 minutes.
3 Serve on the hamburger patties.

These patties are very soft and do not have the 'meatiness' of normal hamburger patties. Liesbet and her family are quite happy to eat these hamburgers, but Gabi's family prefer to have normal meat patties. (See Dieticians' notes *on how to do this and still have a low GI meal.)*

Dieticians' notes

- Commercial bread rolls have a very high GI, so ideally one should only eat half a roll. Because we have made the patties with half beans and half mince, and we have included a low GI BBQ sauce, the effect of the high GI rolls is lessened.
- To keep the GI below 60 and the GL around about 20 for the whole meal, the patties, as well as the BBQ sauce, must be eaten preferably with only half a roll. If a whole roll is eaten, the GI will go up to 58 and the GL to 30!
- Brown and white rolls have a similar GI, although brown rolls contain slightly more fibre.
- For those who do not like the bean and meat patties, the alternative is to have a grilled lean-meat patty, on a bun made from the recipe for Breakfast oat baps (page 32).
- The BBQ sauce must be included to keep the GI low.
- Do *not* butter the rolls.
- These hamburgers make a good **carbo-loading** meal.
- **Slimmers** please note that one hamburger patty and sauce makes up your whole meal. Add a large tossed salad to fill your plate, and omit the roll entirely.

Alternatively

- Use the recipe for Mini meatballs (page 96) to make 8 hamburger patties, and use ordinary bread rolls. The GI of these patties plus a roll is 57, and the GL 27.
- Do *not* butter the rolls.
- Normal commercial hamburgers contain about 8 times the amount of fat, no fibre and the GI and GL are very high.

Nutrients per patty + sauce

GI low (43) • Fat 6 g • Carbohydrate 23 g • Fibre 5 g • Protein 11 g • kJ 834

ONE PATTY WITH BBQ SAUCE IS EQUIVALENT TO 1 STARCH AND 1 1/2 PROTEIN AND VEGETABLE
GL 9

Nutrients per patty + sauce and 1/2 roll

GI low (54) • Fat 6 g • Carbohydrate 37 g • Fibre 6 g • Protein 14 g • kJ 1134
GL 20

French bread pizza

Serves 6

1 French bread (400 g)
1/2 x 410 g tin baked beans in tomato sauce
125 ml (1/2 c) oat bran
5 ml (1 t) canola or olive oil
1 onion, peeled and chopped
1/4 green pepper, seeded and chopped
5 ml (1 t) dried Italian herb mix
1 ml (1/4 t) dried crushed garlic
2 tomatoes, chopped
5 ml (1 t) mustard powder
125 g (1/2 packet) lean bacon, fat removed, chopped
250 ml (1 c) grated low-fat Mozzarella cheese

Nutrients per serving

GI intermediate (58) • Fat 7 g • Carbohydrate 30 g • Fibre 5 g • Protein 14 g • kJ 986

ONE SERVING IS EQUIVALENT TO 2 STARCH AND 2 LEAN PROTEIN
GL 17

1. Preheat the oven to 180 °C.
2. Slice the French bread lengthwise and remove the inside from both halves. Discard 375 ml (1 1/2 c) of the centre of the bread. Mix the leftover crumbled bread centre with the beans and oat bran.
3. Heat the oil and gently fry the onion, green pepper, herbs and garlic. Add the tomatoes and cook until soft.
4. Mix the bread and beans with the onion and tomato mixture, and add the mustard. Pile the mixture into the bread halves. Sprinkle with bacon and, lastly, top with the cheese.
5. Place on a greased baking sheet and bake for 15 minutes.
6. Serve with a large tossed salad.

Dieticians' notes

- French bread has a high GI, therefore it is very important to remove some of the inside of the bread and replace it with the low GI oat bran and beans.
- Anything made with flour as the main ingredient will have a high GI. This pizza version has a lower GI and fat content. Most **takeaways** are *high* GI and *high* fat.
- **Slimmers:** Do not add more starch or protein.

Bacon and broccoli quiche

Serves 8

250 ml (1 c) flour, sifted before measuring
125 ml (1/2 c) oat bran
45 ml (3 T) 'lite' margarine
1 ml (1/4 t) salt
1 egg
45 ml (3 T) ice water

FILLING

1 x 410 g tin white beans, drained
250 ml (1 c) broccoli florets, cut into small pieces
125 g (1/2 packet) lean bacon, chopped
1 large onion, peeled and finely chopped
3 eggs
100 ml (2/5 c) skim milk
150 ml (3/5 c) plain, low-fat yoghurt
salt and pepper to taste
2 ml (1/2 t) mustard powder
125 ml (1/2 c) Mozzarella cheese, grated
5 ml (1 t) grated Parmesan cheese

Nutrients per serving

GI low (51) • Fat 10 g • Carbohydrate 30 g • Fibre 5 g • Protein 14 g • kJ 1 196

ONE SERVING IS EQUIVALENT TO 2 PROTEIN, 1 1/2 STARCH, AND VEGETABLE
GL 15

1. For the base, rub together the flour, oat bran, margarine and salt until the mixture resembles breadcrumbs.
2. Combine egg and water. Add 15 ml (1 T) egg mixture at a time to the flour mixture and mix to a soft dough. Add more flour if it becomes sticky. Cover and chill for about 20 minutes.
3. Roll out and line a greased French flan dish or pie dish, or press the dough into the dish with your fingers.
4. For the filling, drain the beans, mash finely and spread evenly over the base of the quiche. Sprinkle the broccoli evenly over the mashed beans.
5. Fry the bacon and onion without adding any oil or other fat to the pan. If it sticks, add a little water and stir.
6. Beat the eggs, milk and yoghurt together. Add salt, pepper and mustard powder to taste. Add the onion and bacon to the egg mixture, stir and pour over the quiche. Sprinkle with cheeses.
7. Bake at 180 °C for 25–30 minutes until the filling is firm.
8. Serve with a mixed salad for a complete meal.

Dieticians' notes

- Even though we have used skim milk and low-fat yoghurt and no frying is involved, the fat is still 10 g per portion.
- **Quiches are very high in fat**, especially those that are commercially prepared.

Chicken with curried rice

Serves 4

3 deboned chicken breasts, skinned (about 450 g)
5 ml (1 t) canola or olive oil
1 large onion, peeled and finely chopped
1 stalk celery, sliced
1 carrot, grated
6 sprigs fresh parsley, finely chopped
125 ml (1/2 c) dry white wine
10 ml (2 t) tomato paste
125 ml (1/2 c) prepared chicken stock (1/4 stock cube or 5 ml [1 t] stock powder)
pepper to taste
1 bay leaf
375 ml (1 1/2 c) water
125 g (1/2 c) basmati rice, uncooked
5 ml (1 t) 'lite' margarine
2 ml (1/2 t) salt
5 ml (1 t) curry powder
20 g (3 T) grated Parmesan cheese

Nutrients per serving
GI low (52) • Fat 7 g • Carbohydrate 32 g • Fibre 2 g • Protein 30 g • kJ 1 434

ONE SERVING IS EQUIVALENT TO 2 STARCH AND 3 PROTEIN
GL 17

1. Cut the chicken into 1 cm cubes.
2. Heat the oil in a saucepan or non-stick frying pan. Add the vegetables and parsley and stir-fry gently for about 10 minutes.
3. Add the chicken and cook, stirring for 4–5 minutes.
4. Stir in the combined wine, tomato paste and stock. Season with pepper and add the bay leaf.
5. Bring to a boil, reduce the heat and simmer gently for about 15 minutes. Remove the bay leaf before serving.
6. To cook the rice: add rice to the water in a saucepan and bring to a boil, then simmer, half covered, for 18–20 minutes or until the water is absorbed.
7. Add the margarine, salt and curry powder. Stir until combined. Place the rice in a warmed serving dish, top with the chicken sauce and sprinkle with the Parmesan cheese. Serve with 2–3 cooked vegetables.

Dieticians' notes

- Parmesan cheese is high in saturated fat. In this recipe only 5 g per portion is used, and the flavour enhancement it gives is worth the little extra fat.
- Add extra chopped vegetables to the chicken sauce, if desired.

Chicken casserole

Serves 8

8 chicken thighs, ± 100 g each, skinned
1 onion, peeled and finely chopped
1 x 410 g tin baked beans in tomato sauce
1 green pepper, seeded and chopped
15 ml (1 T) raw honey
2 ml (1/2 t) mustard powder
5 ml (1 t) mixed herbs
1/2 chicken stock cube. or 10 ml (2 t) chicken stock
200 ml (4/5 c) boiled water (for stock)
4 rashers lean bacon (salt-reduced)
60 ml (4 T) chopped parsley

Nutrients per serving (with rice)
GI low (55) • Fat 7 g • Carbohydrate 34 g • Fibre 5 g • Protein 23 g • kJ 1 258

ONE SERVING IS EQUIVALENT TO 1 1/2 STARCH AND 2 1/2 PROTEIN
GL 19

1. Arrange the chicken thighs in an oven dish. Mix the rest of the ingredients, except the bacon and parsley, and spoon the mixture over the chicken thighs.
2. Cover and bake for 1 hour in a preheated oven at 180 °C, turning the chicken a few times.
3. Remove the cover and bake for another 30 minutes.
4. Remove all visible fat from the bacon and grill until crisp.
5. Mix the grilled bacon and the parsley and sprinkle over the chicken casserole.
6. Serve with rice or durum wheat pasta (180 ml [3/4 c] per person), and vegetables.

This is a delicious, quick casserole to prepare but needs to bake for 1 1/2 hours.

Dieticians' notes

- Commercial honey has a very high GI, so only a little should be used in combination with lots of other low GI ingredients.
- The portion size of this dish is ideal for women. Men may have 1 1/2 portions. Remember to add 1 portion starch for each 125 ml (1/2 c) portion cooked basmati rice or pasta.

Curried chicken dish

Serves 5

400 g sweet potato, cooked and cubed
500 g cooked chicken, deboned, skin removed and cubed
5 ml (1 t) canola or olive oil
1 large onion, peeled and finely chopped
5 ml (1 t) minced garlic
5-10 ml (1–2 t) curry powder, to taste
3 ml (1/2 t) turmeric
5 ml (1 t) chicken spice
2 ml (1/2 t) salt
60 ml (1/4 c) brown grape vinegar
250 ml (1 c) water
15 ml (1 T) apricot jam

Nutrients per serving

GI low (51) • Fat 8 g • Carbohydrate 21 g • Fibre 3 g • Protein 29 g • kJ 1 204

ONE SERVING IS EQUIVALENT TO 1 STARCH, 2 1/2 PROTEIN AND VEGETABLE
GL 11

1. First prepare the sauce by heating oil in a non-stick pan and gently frying the onion until golden brown. Add the garlic and spices, and stir well to combine.
2. Add the vinegar, water and apricot jam. Add the cooked sweet potato and 125 ml (1/2 c) of the water they were cooked in. Add the cubed chicken and simmer for half an hour.
3. Slightly mash one third of the sweet potato, just enough to thicken the gravy.
4. Serve with rice (if desired), sambals such as chopped onion and tomato, cucumber in natural low-fat yoghurt, and 'lite' chutney.

Dieticians' notes

- The sweet potato gives the curry a rich flavour, and is lower in GI than ordinary potatoes.
- The GI of this meal is calculated without the sambals. If these are eaten, the GI would drop even further.
- The nutrients per serving do not include the rice. Remember to add 1 starch for each 1/2 cup of cooked rice that is eaten.
- **Slimmers**, this is a meal in itself. Skip the rice and have it with the sambals, as the sweet potato already contains starch.

Malayan chicken

Serves 4

4 chicken breasts, skin removed
5 ml (1 t) canola or olive oil
1 onion, peeled and chopped
1 x 410 g tin small white or butter beans, drained
15 ml (1 T) cornflour (see *Dieticians' notes*)
15 ml (1 T) curry powder
15 ml (1 T) 'lite' chutney or ordinary chutney
300 ml (1 1/5 c) unsweetened orange juice
2 ml (1/2 t) salt
1 large green banana

Nutrients per serving

GI low (43) • Fat 7 g • Carbohydrate 32 g • Fibre 7 g • Protein 39 g • kJ 1521

ONE SERVING IS EQUIVALENT TO 3 LEAN PROTEIN, 1 FRUIT AND 1 STARCH
GL 14

1. Cut the chicken into cubes. Heat the oil in a frying pan, add the chicken and onion and brown.
2. Mash the beans lightly, add with the remaining ingredients – except the banana – to the chicken, and mix lightly. Spoon the mixture into a casserole dish and bake for 40 minutes in a preheated oven at 180 °C.
3. Add the sliced banana 10 minutes before serving.
4. Serve hot on rice, cooked pearl barley or a mixture of the two (if desired), with 2–3 cooked vegetables or a tossed salad.

This is a quick and easy dish for those rushed days when supper needs to be on the table in a hurry.

Dieticians' notes

- To **thicken sauces and gravies**, keep a jar with a mixture of half oat bran and half flour. This has a lower GI than flour, cornflour or gravy powder, which is normally used. Alternatively, lower GI oats, mashed beans or split lentils could be used as thickeners.
- Using chicken in a recipe always gives a higher protein content and helps to keep the fat content lower.
- The bonus is that this dish is high in fibre, so often lacking in our meals today.
- Normally we discourage the use of cornflour for thickening sauces and gravies because of its high GI. But in this recipe the amount used is so little, and there are so many other low GI ingredients, that it hardly has an effect on the GI.
- **Slimmers** should omit the rice as the beans already contain starch.

Pasta with broccoli and chicken

Serves 4

5 ml (1 t) canola or olive oil
3 chicken breasts (150 g each), cut into thin strips
150 g tube pasta: e.g. penne (500 ml [2 c] raw)
1 onion, peeled and sliced
1 red pepper, seeded and sliced into thin strips
5 ml (1 t) crushed garlic
1 x 410 g tin tomatoes, diced
1/2 chicken stock cube, dissolved in
250 ml (1 c) boiling water
45 ml (3 T) sultanas
2 ml (1/2 t) grated orange rind
1 litre (4 c) small broccoli florets
5 ml (1 t) cornflour
10 ml (2 t) brown sugar
15 ml (1 T) balsamic vinegar (optional)

Nutrients per serving

GI low (34) • Fat 6 g • Carbohydrate 37 g • Fibre 7 g • Protein 33 g • kJ 1 432

One serving is equivalent to 2 starch, 3 protein and vegetable
GL 13

1. In a large non-stick frying pan, heat oil over medium heat until hot but not smoking. Add chicken and cook, stirring, until lightly browned. With a slotted spoon, transfer chicken to a plate.
2. Cook the pasta in lightly salted boiling water until just tender.
3. Meanwhile, add the onion, red pepper and garlic to the frying pan and cook, stirring, until the onion is transparent.
4. Add the tomatoes and their juice, stock, sultanas, orange rind and a little freshly ground black pepper and bring to the boil. Simmer until the sauce is slightly reduced.
5. Add the broccoli and cook until tender, about 5 minutes.
6. In a small bowl, combine the cornflour, sugar and vinegar. Return the chicken to the pan and stir in the cornflour mixture. Cook until the sauce is slightly thickened and the chicken is heated through. Toss the chicken with the hot, cooked pasta and serve with a salad.

This is a rather different, sweet-and-sour tomato pasta sauce. Freezing the chicken breasts for about 15 minutes will make it easier to slice them thinly.

Dieticians' note

- Normally we discourage the use of cornflour for thickening sauces because of its high GI, but in this recipe very little is used and there are many other low GI ingredients.

Chicken spaghetti bolognaise

Serves 4

150 g durum wheat spaghetti (bundle size of R5 coin [2.5 cm in diameter])
1 x 65 g pork sausage, casing removed
1/2 chicken stock cube, or 10 ml (2 t) stock powder
3 chicken breasts (about 150 g each), chopped finely
10 ml (2 t) crushed garlic
1 x 410 g tin chopped tomatoes with juice
125 ml (1/2 c) parsley, chopped
freshly ground black pepper
10 ml (2 t) sugar
250 ml (1 c) frozen peas or mange tout (sugar snap peas)
60 g (2 matchboxes) low-fat Mozzarella cheese, grated

Nutrients per serving

GI low (34) • Fat 10 g • Carbohydrate 41 g • Fibre 6 g • Protein 37 g • kJ 1 714

One serving is equivalent to 1 1/2 starch, 3 protein, and vegetable
GL 13

1. Cook the spaghetti in lightly salted boiling water until tender but still firm.
2. Meanwhile, crumble the sausage meat into a large frying pan. Add a little water and cook over medium heat, stirring, until the sausage is no longer pink.
3. Add the stock powder, chicken and garlic. Cook, stirring, for about 4 minutes until the chicken is no longer pink.
4. Stir in the tomatoes with their juices, parsley, pepper and sugar and bring to the boil. Simmer for about 5 minutes.
5. Add the peas and cook until just heated through.
6. Toss the sauce with the hot pasta, sprinkle with Mozzarella cheese and serve immediately with a salad.

Dieticians' notes

- Using sugar does not raise the GI of the dish as so little is used.
- It is important to use pasta made from durum wheat as it has a much lower GI than home-made pasta made from cake flour.
- The fat content is lowered considerably by using chicken breasts instead of beef mince.

Chicken stir-fry

Serves 6

5 ml (1 t) canola or olive oil
4 chicken breasts, cut into thin slices
2 onions, peeled and sliced
2 stalks celery, chopped
250 g (1 punnet) mushrooms, sliced
750 ml (3 c) shredded cabbage
125 ml (1/2 c) broccoli florets
125 ml (1/2 c) cauliflower florets
1 large carrot, cut into julienne strips
1 green pepper, seeded and cut into strips
1 x 410g tin butter beans, drained

SAUCE

30 ml (2 T) reduced-salt soya sauce
30 ml (2 T) vinegar
15 ml (1 T) crushed garlic
5 ml (1 t) ground ginger
15 ml (1 T) sugar
20 ml (4 t) tomato sauce, ordinary or 'lite'
30 ml (2 T) cornflour
30 ml (2 T) oat bran
375 ml (1 1/2 c) water

1. Heat the oil in a wok or large frying pan. Gently stir-fry the onions until transparent.
2. Add the chicken and stir-fry until browned.
3. Add all the shredded and chopped vegetables and stir-fry until just cooked. Add the butter beans and heat through.
4. For the sauce, mix all the ingredients and stir until lump free.
5. Pour the sauce over the stir-fry and stir well so that the sauce thickens evenly.
6. Serve with rice or cooked pearl barley (125–250 ml [1/2–1 c] per person).

Dieticians' notes

- Any lower GI rice can be used i.e. basmati, brown or Tastic.
- **Mushrooms** are not recommended for those suffering from gout.
- For a **carbo-loading** meal, leave out the chicken and have a double portion of stir-fry with lots of rice or barley. The stir-fry would then yield 27 g carbohydrate (901 kJ), and each 125 ml (1/2 c) rice or barley would yield another 28 g carbohydrate.

Nutrients per serving (with basmati rice)
GI low (56) • Fat 5 g • Carbohydrate 41 g • Fibre 8 g • Protein 31 g • kJ 1491

ONE SERVING IS EQUIVALENT TO 1 1/2 STARCH, 4 PROTEIN AND VEGETABLE
GL 20

Tagliatelle with chicken

Serves 4

5 ml (1 t) canola or olive oil
1 onion, peeled and finely diced
5 ml (1 t) minced garlic, or 2 ml (1/2 t) dried garlic flakes
3 chicken breasts, finely chopped (±150 g each)
125 ml (1/2 c) dry white wine
1/2 chicken stock cube dissolved in
180 ml (3/4 c) boiling water
250 g mushrooms, quartered (1 punnet)
1 x 410 g tin Italian tomatoes, chopped
7.5 ml (1 1/2 t) sage, dried
1 small bay leaf
5 ml (1 t) sugar
pepper to taste
150 g durum wheat tagliatelle (1/3 of 500 g packet)
10 ml (2 t) finely grated Parmesan cheese

1. In a large non-stick frying pan heat the oil until hot but not smoking. Add the onion and garlic and cook, stirring until the onions become transparent.
2. Add the chicken and cook, stirring to break up the meat, for about 5 minutes or until the chicken is no longer pink.
3. Add the wine and cook until almost evaporated and then add the stock, mushrooms, tomatoes with their juices, sage, bay leaf, sugar and pepper and bring to the boil.
4. Reduce heat to a simmer, cover and cook for about 20 minutes until the sauce is richly flavoured and thickened.
5. Meanwhile, cook the pasta until just tender. Drain well.
6. Toss the sauce with the hot pasta. Divide into 4 portions, sprinkle with Parmesan and serve with a salad.

Dieticians' note

- Double the pasta for a good **carbo-loading** dish with 59 g sustained release carbohydrate, and limited fat and protein

Nutrients per serving
GI low (38) • Fat 6 g • Carbohydrate 32 g • Fibre 3 g • Protein 31 g • kJ 1 374

ONE SERVING IS EQUIVALENT TO 1 1/2 STARCH, 3 PROTEIN AND VEGETABLE
GL 12

Mexican fish and beans

Serves 4

5 ml (1 t) canola or olive oil
1 stalk celery, finely diced
1 onion, peeled and finely chopped
5 ml (1 t) minced garlic (1 clove, crushed)
1 x 410 g tin tomatoes, undrained and mashed
1 x 410 g tin white beans, well drained
5 ml (1 t) minced chilli
125 ml (1/2 c) dry white wine
4 deboned white fish fillets (about 500 g), cut into cubes
30 ml (2 T) chopped fresh parsley
freshly ground black pepper

1. Heat the oil in a non-stick frying pan or saucepan.
2. Add the celery, onion and garlic and sauté for about 5 minutes or until soft.
3. Add the tomatoes, beans and chilli.
4. Simmer, uncovered, for 10 minutes.
5. Meanwhile, heat the wine in a medium-sized saucepan over moderate heat.
6. Add the fish, and poach gently for 3-4 minutes, or until just cooked through.
7. Combine the cooked fish and cooking juices with the tomato and bean mixture.
8. Add the parsley, and pepper to taste.
9. Serve immediately with mashed potato or 'pap' (stiff mealie meal porridge), and a mixed salad.

The mashed potatoes should be prepared using only low-fat or fat-free milk and very little 'lite' margarine.
The 'pap' should be made from unsifted mealie meal.

Hint

To thaw frozen fish steaks, and retain that fresh-from-the-sea flavour, place them in milk and be sure to dry them well before baking.
Chilli baked beans can be substituted for the white beans in this recipe.

Dieticians' notes

- This meal is a typical example of when a high GI food, such as mashed potatoes, can successfully be combined with a low GI dish containing legumes/beans. The GI of the fish and bean dish alone is 18, and the GI of mashed potatoes is 71. Together, the meal has a GI of 50.
- The nutrient analysis of the fish *with* the mashed potatoes or 'pap' is alongside.
- 'Pap' and mashed potatoes have similar GI values.
- It is interesting to note that if the mealie meal porridge ('pap') is cooked a few hours before and allowed to cool and is then reheated when the fish is ready to eat, the GI of the 'pap' is lowered by at least 10 points. We recommend that if time allows, you make the porridge beforehand and allow it to cool. Reheat it just before serving.

Nutrients per serving
(with mash/unsifted mealie meal)
GI low (50) • Fat 8 g • Carbohydrate 37 g • Fibre 8 g • Protein 31 g • kJ 1 640

ONE SERVING OF FISH AND POTATO OR 'PAP' IS EQUIVALENT TO 2 STARCH AND 3 PROTEIN
GL 19

Fish cakes

Makes 6 large fish cakes or 18 small fish cakes
A quick and easy dish that is also easy on the pocket

1 x 410 g tin salmon or pilchards in tomato sauce
1 onion, peeled and finely grated
10 ml (2 t) finely chopped parsley
250 ml (1 c) lower GI oats
1 egg
15 ml (1 T) or less canola or olive oil

1. Remove fish from the sauce and flake the fish. Add the onion, parsley and oats.
2. Mix with the egg and some of the sauce from the fish to make a firm mixture. Be careful not to overmix.
3. Shape the mixture into 6 large or 18 small fish cakes or patties.
4. Heat the oil and fry quickly.
5. Serve with baby (new) jacket potatoes sprinkled with parsley and 2–3 cooked vegetables, or with a large mixed salad.

Dieticians' notes

- Use this recipe for fish burger patties. Because the GI of the patties is so low, they can be eaten with an ordinary bread roll!
- Remember not to butter the roll, to keep the fat content down. Tomato sauce, mustard and/or 'lite' chutney can be added.
- Pilchards are a rich source of omega-3 essential fatty acids. Modern diets are usually lacking in omega-3 fatty acids so this is a pleasant way to include such a rich source once a week. Omega-3 fatty acids are especially important for allergy-prone people and those with compromised immune systems. Omega-3 fatty acids are also shown to be beneficial in ADHD, heart disease and inflammatory diseases such as arthritis.

Nutrients per large fish cake

GI low (36) • Fat 6 g • Carbohydrate 3 g • Fibre 0,5 g • Protein 13 g • kJ 510

ONE LARGE FISH CAKE (PATTY) IS EQUIVALENT TO 2 PROTEIN
GL 1

Country-style tuna bake

Serves 4

125 g durum wheat screw noodles (uncooked)
5 ml (1 t) canola or olive oil
1 onion, peeled and chopped
125 g sliced mushrooms (1/2 punnet)
15 ml (1 T) flour
15 ml (1 T) tomato purée
125 ml (1/2 c) low-fat milk or skim milk
pinch of dried basil
1 ml (1/4 t) salt
freshly ground black pepper
1 x 170 g tin tuna in brine, drained
60 g (2 matchboxes) low-fat Cheddar cheese, grated
10 ml (2 t) grated Parmesan cheese

1. Preheat the oven to 180 °C.
2. Cook the pasta in plenty of boiling, lightly salted water until just tender. Drain and set aside.
3. Heat the oil and sauté the onions and mushrooms, stirring frequently.
4. Blend in the flour and add the tomato purée.
5. Mix in the milk, basil, salt and pepper. Continue stirring until the mixture thickens.
6. Combine with the cooked pasta and tuna.
7. Pour the mixture into an ovenproof dish and sprinkle with the Cheddar and Parmesan cheese.
8. Bake in preheated oven for 25–30 minutes.
9. For a complete meal, serve with a large mixed salad.

Dieticians' notes

- By doubling up the quantity of the noodles, this is a delicious **carbo-loading** meal. The carbohydrate content will go up to 50 g per portion, but the protein, fat and GI would remain as low as they are.
- Normally we do not recommend flour for thickening of sauces as it has a high GI. But in this recipe, the low GI milk and pasta offset the small amount of flour used.
- The higher fat content of this fish dish, despite using so little tuna in brine, is due to the inclusion of milk and cheese. It can be lowered slightly by using skim milk.

Nutrients per serving

GI low (38) • Fat 8 g • Carbohydrate 28 g • Fibre 2 g • Protein 18 g • kJ 1 071

ONE SERVING IS EQUIVALENT TO 1 STARCH, 2 PROTEIN AND VEGETABLE
GL 11

Curried fish and rice

Serves 6

400 g frozen hake fillets
5 ml (1 t) fish spice
250 ml (1 c) low-fat milk or skim milk
1 medium onion, peeled and chopped
5 ml (1 t) canola or olive oil
5–7 ml (1–1½ t) curry powder
1 ml (¼ t) turmeric
125 ml (½ c) low GI rice, uncooked
2 ml (½ t) salt
2 hard-boiled eggs
rind and juice of 1 lemon
1 x 410 g tin lentils, or 250 ml (1 c) cooked lentils
125 ml (½ c) low-fat yoghurt
2 ml (½ t) lemon pepper

Nutrients per serving

GI low (43) • Fat 5 g • Carbohydrate 26 g • Fibre 4 g • Protein 21 g • kJ 1 035

ONE SERVING IS EQUIVALENT TO 1 STARCH AND 2 PROTEIN
GL 11

1. Skin the fish fillets and put them in a saucepan. Sprinkle with the fish spice. Pour milk over, cover and cook for 10 minutes.
2. Drain, retaining the cooking juices. Add enough water to the cooking juices to make 600 ml.
3. Flake the fish, removing the fish bones.
4. Fry the onion in the oil until soft. Add the curry powder and turmeric. Add the rice, salt and milk and water mixture. Stir well. Simmer for 20 minutes or until the rice is done.
5. Meanwhile, shell the eggs and cut into wedges.
6. Add the eggs, fish, lemon rind, juice and lentils to the rice mixture. Mix lightly, and gently heat through.
7. Add the yoghurt, mix and heat for a few seconds. (Be careful – if the dish gets too hot the yoghurt will curdle.)
8. Sprinkle with lemon pepper and serve hot or cold with salad or cooked vegetables.

Dieticians' note

- All fish dishes have a low fat content, as fish is a very lean source of protein.

Bean casserole with pizza topping

Serves 4

5 ml (1 t) olive or canola oil
2 onions, peeled and chopped
2 green peppers, seeded and chopped
1 x 410 g tin brown or sugar beans
250 ml (1 c) cooked, brown rice
60 ml (4 T) chopped parsley
2 thin slices fresh brown bread, crumbled
2 eggs (1 whole egg + 1 egg white)
125 ml (½ c) plain, low-fat yoghurt
3 tomatoes, thinly sliced
60 g (2 matchboxes) Mozzarella cheese, grated
30 ml (2 T) grated Parmesan cheese
2 ml (½ t) dried origanum
1 ml (¼ t) dried basil
5 ml (1 t) olive oil

Nutrients per serving

GI low (37) • Fat 9 g • Carbohydrate 42 g • Fibre 10 g • Protein 17 g • kJ 1 406

ONE PORTION IS EQUIVALENT TO 3 STARCH AND 2 PROTEIN OR 2 STARCH AND 3 PROTEIN
GL 15

1. Preheat the oven to 180 °C.
2. Heat the oil and sauté the onion and green pepper until soft. Set aside.
3. Drain the beans and mix with the rice, parsley, breadcrumbs, onions and green pepper.
4. Beat the egg and yoghurt together and season with a little salt and pepper.
5. Add the bean mixture. Mix well.
6. Spoon into a greased ovenproof dish and spread evenly.
7. Cover with tomato slices and mixed grated cheeses.
8. Sprinkle with the herbs and, lastly, with olive oil.
9. Bake for 25 minutes until the cheese bubbles.

Dieticians' notes

- **Vegetarian dishes** are often perceived to be low fat owing to the lack of meat, fish or chicken. They are, in fact, usually very **high in fat**. This dish only has such a low fat content because we have limited the oil and cheese to a minimum.
- This dish makes a **good carbo-loading** meal. It is high in slowly absorbed carbohydrates and neither the fat nor the protein is too high.
- Bread is a high GI ingredient that has been offset by all the other low GI ingredients.
- This dish contains both egg and dairy, therefore it is suitable for **lacto-ovo vegetarians**.

Vegetable lasagne

Serves 6

1 bunch (500 g) spinach, washed and stalks removed
200 g instant durum wheat lasagne sheets
10 ml (2 t) grated Parmesan cheese
60 g (2 matchboxes) lower-fat Mozzarella cheese, grated

VEGETABLE SAUCE
5 ml (1 t) canola or olive oil
2 onions, peeled and chopped
10 ml (2 t) minced garlic
250 g (1 punnet) mushrooms, sliced
1/2 small green pepper, seeded and chopped
1 x 410 g tin mixed beans, drained
1 x 410 g tin tomatoes with juice, mashed
5 ml (1 t) dried mixed herbs

CHEESE SAUCE
5 ml (1 t) 'lite' margarine
375 ml (1 1/2 c) low-fat milk
20 ml (4 t) flour
60 g (2 matchboxes) low-fat cheese
pinch of ground nutmeg
2 ml (1/2 t) salt
freshly ground black pepper to taste

1. Lightly steam the spinach until just wilted, then drain well.
2. For the vegetable sauce, heat the oil in a non-stick frying pan. Add the onions and garlic and cook for about 5 minutes.
3. Add the mushrooms and green pepper and cook for a further 3 minutes. Add the beans, tomatoes and herbs. Simmer for 15 minutes.
4. For the cheese sauce, melt the margarine, and stir in the milk.
5. In a 500 ml (2 c) glass bowl or jug, mix the flour with 45 ml (3 T) water to a smooth paste. Remove the hot milk from the heat and gradually add the milk, 45 ml (3 T) at a time, to the flour paste, stirring after each addition until smooth. Pour the sauce back into the saucepan.
6. Return to heat and stir until sauce is smooth and thickened. Remove from heat and stir in cheese, nutmeg, salt and pepper.
7. To assemble, pour half the vegetable sauce over the base of a lasagne dish. Cover with a layer of lasagne sheets, then half the spinach. Spread half the cheese sauce over the spinach. Top with remaining vegetable sauce and lasagne sheets. Cover with remaining spinach and finish with the remaining cheese sauce. Sprinkle with Parmesan and Mozzarella cheese.
8. Bake in a preheated oven at 180 °C for 45 minutes to 1 hour until bubbly and brown.

Although this recipe looks quite long, it is in fact very easy to prepare and well worth the effort. It is quite delicious for a vegetarian meal. To soften the lasagne sheets and prevent them from curling up, dip each sheet in hot water as you assemble the dish.

Dieticians' notes

- This dish has an exceptionally high fibre content and is also very low in fat.
- It is important to use durum wheat pasta as it has a low GI.

Why do we add dry beans (legumes) to so many dishes?

Most of us do not know how to use legumes any more. To help you see how easy it is to include them in everyday meals, we have added them in tasty and easy ways to many of our recipes. When using dried beans in a recipe for the first time, mash the drained beans – or liquidise them with a little water – and then add to the dish. This helps to 'hide' them better, so that one gets used to their texture gradually. Beans (and all legumes) have many health advantages:

- Legumes actively bind cholesterol.
- Legumes can lower morning blood glucose readings in those with diabetes.
- Legumes are rich in soluble and insoluble fibre and thereby help in Irritable Bowel Syndrome.
- Legumes are very effective in lowering the GI of any meal.
- Legumes increase the satiety value of meals, and are therefore effective in slimming diets.
- The soluble fibre in legumes stimulates the immune system in the bowel.
- Legumes are a quick and easy way to increase the fibre content of any meal.
- Legumes are low in fat, a definite advantage in our age of high-fat fast foods.
- They are also an inexpensive source of protein.

Nutrients per serving

GI low (37) • Fat 7 g • Carbohydrate 44 g • Fibre 11 g • Protein 19 g • kJ 1 367

ONE SERVING IS EQUIVALENT TO 2 STARCH, 2 PROTEIN AND 2 VEGETABLES

GL 16

Vegetable curry

Serves 6

5 ml (1 t) canola or olive oil
1 medium onion, peeled and chopped
10 ml (2 t) minced garlic
22 ml (1½ T) minced ginger
10 ml (2 t) ground cumin
10 ml (2 t) turmeric
10 ml (2 t) curry powder
2 ml (½ t) minced chilli, optional
3 ml (½ t) salt
125 ml (½ c) water
1 large potato, unpeeled, cut into cubes
500 ml (2 c) cubed pumpkin
250 ml (1 c) cauliflower florets
1 x 410 g tin tomatoes with juices, chopped
1 x 410 g tin chickpeas, drained
1 red pepper, thickly sliced
4 baby marrows (zucchini), thickly sliced
30 ml (2 T) fresh coriander

CREAMY SAUCE

5 ml (1 t) 'lite' margarine
½ vegetable stock cube, dissolved in
250 ml (1 c) boiling water
125 ml (½ c) low-fat evaporated milk
20 ml (4 t) flour

Nutrients per serving
(without basmati rice)
GI low (40) • Fat 4 g • Carbohydrate 25 g • Fibre 7 g • Protein 8 g • kJ 753

ONE SERVING IS EQUIVALENT TO 1 STARCH, 1 PROTEIN AND 2 VEGETABLES
GL 10

1. Heat the oil in a large saucepan, add the onion and garlic and gently fry until soft.
2. Add the spices and cook for 1 minute. Add the water, potato, pumpkin, cauliflower, tomatoes and chickpeas. Simmer for 20 minutes.
3. Add the sliced red pepper and baby marrows and simmer for another 10 minutes.
4. Meanwhile, prepare the creamy sauce. Melt margarine in a small saucepan. When hot, add the stock, water and milk.
5. In a glass bowl, mix the flour to a smooth paste with 45 ml (3 T) water. When the milk and stock are hot, pour half of it into the flour paste and stir well.
6. Pour the flour and milk mixture back into the saucepan with the other half of the milk and stock and bring to the boil, stirring until thick and creamy.
7. Add the sauce to the curried vegetables and mix gently. Add the fresh coriander.
8. Serve on basmati rice.

Dieticians' notes

- Normally one would expect a vegetable curry to have only vegetable portions. However, the creamy sauce and chickpeas both contribute appreciable amounts of protein. The chickpeas, potato and vegetables contribute starch, so this vegetarian dish can be counted as protein and starch with vegetables. Add one portion starch per person for each 125 ml (½ c) cooked basmati rice that is added to one serving of this curry.
- Also take note that we have skimped on the amount of oil and 'lite' margarine used, and insisted on low-fat evaporated milk to keep the fat content of the dish low. Most vegetarian dishes are high in fat despite the fact that no meat, fish or chicken is used.
- It is important to use the chickpeas, otherwise the GI of the dish may be raised too much due to the use of the higher GI potato and pumpkin.
- Any other dried beans may be used in place of the chickpeas.
- All vegetables have such a small carbohydrate content that even if they are high GI, they do not influence the GI of any mixed meal significantly.
- This dish can be made up to 3 days in advance and served cold as a 'salad'. Perfect for camping, self-catering holidays and picnics.

Bean and noodle casserole

Serves 4

5 ml (1 t) canola or olive oil
1 onion, peeled and chopped
2 cloves garlic, crushed
1 tomato, chopped
1 x 410 g tin baked beans in tomato sauce
5 ml (1 t) dried origanum
5 ml (1 t) dried basil
200 g (1 tub) fat-free cottage cheese
100 g Mozzarella cheese (3 matchboxes), grated and divided into 2
250 g mushrooms (1 punnet), sliced
1 egg, beaten
750 ml (3 c) cooked durum wheat noodles (1½ c uncooked)

Nutrients per serving

GI low (36) • Fat 10 g • Carbohydrate 52 g • Fibre 11 g • Protein 24 g • kJ 1 608

One serving is equivalent to 3 starch, 2 protein and vegetable

GL 19

1. Preheat the oven to 180 °C.
2. Heat the oil, add the onion and garlic and sauté until soft.
3. Add the tomato, beans and herbs and bring to the boil.
4. Lower the heat and simmer, uncovered, for 10 minutes.
5. Mix the cottage cheese, half the Mozzarella cheese, the mushrooms and egg well.
6. Grease an ovenproof dish, put one half of the noodles into it, top it with half of the cheese mixture and end with half of the bean mixture.
7. Repeat the layers and sprinkle the remaining cheese on top.
8. Bake for 45 minutes in the preheated oven.
9. Serve hot with a green salad or two cooked vegetables.

Dieticians' notes

- It is important to use fat-free cottage cheese, as the Mozzarella already pushes up the fat content.
- The exceptionally high fibre content compensates for the relatively high fat content.
- Vegetarian dishes are usually very high in fat because oil, milk, eggs and cheese are used in abundance.
- This dish is suitable for **carbo-loading**. It is rich in slow-release carbohydrates and the fat and protein are not too high.

Potato and bean pie

Serves 6

2 x 410 g tins brown beans, sugar beans or mixed beans, drained
1 carrot, sliced
1 tomato, diced
250 ml (1 c) cabbage, finely shredded
125 ml (½ c) green beans, chopped
125 ml (½ c) baby marrows, sliced
1 onion, peeled and chopped
1 clove garlic, crushed, or 2 ml (½ t) dried garlic flakes
5 ml (1 t) dried mixed herbs
freshly ground black pepper to taste
30 ml (2 T) cornflour
10 ml (½) stock cube vegetable stock powder, dissolved in 250 ml (1 c) boiling water
30 ml (2 T) BBQ sauce
18 new (baby) potatoes, cooked
20 ml (4 t) 'lite' margarine, melted

1. Preheat the oven to 180 °C.
2. Combine the beans, vegetables and seasoning and place the mixture in an ovenproof dish.
3. Mix the cornflour into the stock and pour the vegetable stock and BBQ sauce over the vegetables and beans.
4. Slice the potatoes and arrange the slices in a layer on top of the bean mixture. Pour the margarine over evenly so all the potatoes are greased.
5. Cover and bake for 45 minutes.
6. Remove the lid and bake for another 15 minutes to brown the potatoes.
7. Serve hot with a green salad to make a complete meal.

Dieticians' notes

- As a rule we do not advocate the use of cornflour for thickening gravies. But in this recipe, so little is used among so many other low GI ingredients, that it has little effect on the GI.
- This makes a good **carbo-loading** meal, which is high in slow-release carbohydrates, with not too much protein and fat.

Nutrients per serving

GI low (46) • Fat 3 g • Carbohydrate 37 g • Fibre 10 g • Protein 10 g • kJ 1 052

One serving is equivalent to 2 starch, 1 protein and vegetable

GL 17

Cheese soufflé

Serves 4

1 x 410 g tin baked beans in tomato sauce
100 ml (2/5 c) oat bran
250 ml (1 c) fresh breadcrumbs (2 slices bread)
3 eggs (1 whole egg + 2 egg whites)
100 ml skim milk
2 ml (1/2 t) crushed garlic
5 ml (1 t) mixed herbs, dried
salt and freshly ground black pepper to taste
60 g low-fat (2 matchboxes) Mozzarella cheese, grated
30 g low-fat (1 matchbox) Cheddar cheese, grated
125 ml (1/2 c) finely chopped parsley

Nutrients per serving

GI low (51) • Fat 8 g • Carbohydrate 30 g • Fibre 9 g • Protein 16 g • kJ 1 074

ONE SERVING IS EQUIVALENT TO 2 STARCH AND 2 PROTEIN
GL 15

1. Preheat the oven to 180 °C.
2. Mash the beans with a fork or process in a food processor or liquidiser until smooth, but not for longer than 1 minute.
3. Mix together the beans, oat bran, fresh breadcrumbs, egg yolk, milk, crushed garlic and herbs until fairly smooth. Do not overmix.
4. Season with salt and pepper.
5. Mix the grated cheeses and parsley and fold two-thirds of the cheeses into the soufflé mix.
6. Whisk the 3 egg whites until stiff peaks form and gently fold into bean mixture. Pour into a greased 16 cm ovenproof soufflé dish and bake for 30 minutes.
7. Sprinkle with the remaining grated cheese and parsley and bake for a further 5 minutes or until the cheese has melted.
8. Serve immediately with a large tossed salad (see Salads, pages 44–52).

This is the ultimate way to disguise baked beans! If you don't tell anybody, no one will even guess that the soufflé contains baked beans. An easy soufflé that does not collapse when taken out of the oven.

Dieticians' notes

- Traditional soufflés are high in fat without any fibre at all.
- This version is much lower in fat and has an incredible fibre content. It is, therefore, very important that you use only **one egg yolk** and **skim milk**.

Savoury bean bake

Serves 5

5 ml (1 t) canola or olive oil
1 onion, peeled and chopped
2 x 410 g tins baked beans in tomato sauce
2 hard-boiled eggs, chopped
30 ml (2 T) parsley, chopped
2 ml (1/2 t) salt
freshly ground black pepper
2 ml (1/2 t) dried marjoram
3 tomatoes, sliced
90 g (3 matchboxes) Mozzarella cheese, grated
1 slice brown bread, crumbed

Nutrients per serving

GI low (46) • Fat 8 g • Carbohydrate 37 g • Fibre 14 g • Protein 15 g • kJ 1 171

ONE SERVING IS EQUIVALENT TO 2 STARCH, 2 PROTEIN AND VEGETABLE
GL 17

1. Heat the oil and sauté the onion until done.
2. Add the beans, eggs, parsley, salt, pepper and marjoram.
3. Turn into a greased ovenproof dish.
4. Garnish with the sliced tomatoes, grated Mozzarella and crumbed bread, and place under a hot grill for 5–10 minutes until crisp and golden brown.

This is a very easy and delicious vegetarian main dish. Serve with a large salad or 2 cooked vegetables.

Dieticians' notes

- Vegetarian dishes are usually very high-fat dishes despite the fact that they do not contain any meat, fish or chicken. Only because the oil and the cheese are so limited in this dish, does it qualify as low-fat.
- This dish has an exceptionally high fibre content, and low fat content.

Macaroni with mushroom sauce

Serves 4

150 g (1½ c) durum wheat macaroni
1 ml (¼ t) salt
SAUCE
5 ml (1 t) olive oil
1 medium onion, peeled and finely sliced
5 ml (1 t) minced garlic (1 clove, crushed)
500 g mushrooms (2 punnets), sliced
5 ml (1 t) paprika
10 ml (2t) Dijon mustard
30 ml (2 T) tomato paste
15 ml (1 T) flour
250 ml (1 c) low-fat evaporated milk
30 g (1 matchbox) lower fat Cheddar cheese, grated
4 chopped spring onions
freshly ground black pepper
30 ml (2 T) freshly chopped parsley
20 ml (4 t) Parmesan cheese

Nutrients per serving

GI low (39) • Fat 7 g • Carbohydrate 42 g • Fibre 4 g • Protein 15 g • kJ 1 208

ONE SERVING IS EQUIVALENT TO 2½ STARCH, AND 2 PROTEIN/DAIRY
GL 16

1. In a large saucepan, cook the pasta, uncovered, in boiling water with 1 ml salt until just tender. Drain and keep warm.
2. Meanwhile, prepare the sauce. Heat the oil in a non-stick frying pan, add the onion, garlic and mushrooms and cook for about 5 minutes or until softened.
3. Combine the paprika, mustard, tomato paste, flour and milk in a small jug. Stir into mushroom mixture with the Cheddar cheese and cook over low heat, stirring frequently, for 5 minutes.
4. Add the spring onions and pepper to taste.
5. Pour the sauce over the pasta and toss gently to combine.
6. Serve sprinkled with parsley and Parmesan cheese.

This dish is quick and easy to put together for a hasty supper. Add a tossed salad, and the meal is complete.

Dieticians' notes

- Parsley is rich in antioxidant vitamins, which protect us from disease, so be generous and use lots.
- For **carbo-loading** use one and half times the amount of pasta with the same amount of sauce. This gives a carbohydrate value of 55 g per portion with a GI of 40. The energy value goes up to 1 463 kJ per portion.
- Always use pasta made from durum wheat – pasta made from ordinary wheat flour has a much higher GI.
- One starch in this dish can be counted as a protein, as protein and starch are equal in calories (kJ).

Creamy vegetarian pasta

Serves 4

150 g (1½ c) durum wheat pasta shells
5 ml (1 t) canola or olive oil
½ onion, peeled and finely chopped
2 carrots, cut into 1 cm cubes
250 ml (1 c) sugar snap peas (mange tout)
500 ml (2 c) cherry tomatoes, halved
3 ml (½ t) dried thyme
salt and freshly ground black pepper
1 x 410 g tin asparagus salad cuts (with water)
10 ml (2 t) cornflour mixed with 20 ml (4 t) water
60 ml (¼ c) fat-reduced cream

Nutrients per serving

GI low (39) • Fat 4 g • Carbohydrate 36 g • Fibre 5 g • Protein 8 g • kJ 861

ONE SERVING IS EQUIVALENT TO 1½ STARCH, 1 PROTEIN AND 2 VEGETABLE
GL 14

1. Cook pasta in lightly salted water until just tender. Drain well.
2. Meanwhile, in a large non-stick frying pan, heat the oil until hot, but not smoking, over medium heat. Add the onion and carrots and cook until the carrots are softened.
3. Add the snap peas and cook gently for 1 minute.
4. Add tomatoes, thyme, a pinch of salt, and pepper. Increase the heat and cook on high until the tomatoes are soft.
5. Add asparagus and its water and bring to the boil. Add the cornflour mixture and cook, stirring until the sauce thickens.
6. Stir in the cream until well blended.
7. Toss the sauce and the hot pasta together and serve.

A lovely light cream sauce that lets the vegetables shine through.

Dieticians' notes

- Asparagus is not suitable for those suffering from gout.
- It is important to use fat-reduced cream in this dish to keep the fat content low.
- This dish is suitable for **carbo-loading** as it contains lots of long-acting carbohydrate with very little fat and protein.

Legal cheese sauce for vegetables

Serves 6

10 ml (2 t) 'lite' margarine (for flavour only)
150 ml (3/5 c) low-fat milk *
150 ml (3/5 c) water from boiling or microwaving vegetables **
1 ml (1/4 t) salt
3 ml (1/2 t) mustard powder
45 ml (3 T) flour
60 g (2 matchboxes) lower fat Cheddar cheese, grated
3 ml (1/2 t) grated Parmesan cheese (optional)

1. Melt the margarine over low heat. Add the milk and vegetable water, then add the salt and mustard powder. Bring to the boil.
2. Meanwhile, mix the flour to a smooth paste with a little water.
3. As soon as the milk boils, pour a little hot milk into the flour mixture and stir well. Pour the flour and water mixture back into the rest of the boiled milk and vegetable water.
4. Return to the heat and boil until the sauce thickens.
5. Add the grated cheeses and pour over the cooked vegetables.

* *Boxed long-life milk gives a creamier sauce without adding extra fat.*
** *Broccoli, cauliflower and courgettes (baby marrow) make the tastiest vegetable water for cheese sauce.*

Dieticians' notes

- Parmesan cheese is high in fat but very strong in flavour. By adding just half a teaspoon to a dish with cheese, one is able to use less than half the amount of cheese – and half the fat – without sacrificing flavour.
- For a plain white sauce, omit the cheeses, add a dash of nutmeg and then it counts as 1/2 starch. This is also lower in fat.
- Note that 60 ml (4 T) cheese sauce has a GL of 2, and 60 ml (4 T) custard (page 106) has a GL of 4. This is due to the extra carbohydrate added to custard in the form of sugar.

Nutrients per serving 60 ml (4 T)
GI low (54) • Fat 5 g • Carbohydrate 4 g • Fibre negligible • Protein 4 g • kJ 316
ONE SERVING IS EQUIVALENT TO 1/2 DAIRY AND 1/2 FAT
GL 2

Roast sweet potatoes or baby potatoes

Serves 4

2 small sweet potatoes or
16 baby/new potatoes
30 ml (2 T) canola or olive oil

1. Cook the sweet potatoes or baby potatoes in their jackets in a microwave or on the stove in boiling water, until just done, but still firm.
2. Preheat the oven to 200 °C.
3. Peel and slice the sweet potatoes, but leave the skins on the new or baby potatoes. The potatoes may be cut in half.
4. Pour oil into a flat baking pan and place into the hot oven. As soon as the oil is hot, after about 5 minutes, remove the pan from the oven and pour **all** the oil out.
5. Place the cooked sweet potatoes or baby potatoes into the baking pan and toss or turn them until completely covered in a thin layer of oil.
6. Roast, turning once, until evenly browned.

Dieticians' notes

- Potatoes have a high GI. But sweet potatoes and baby (new) potatoes with their skin have a lower GI. For this reason we have included a low-fat method of roasting sweet potatoes and baby potatoes to replace high GI, high-fat roast potatoes.
- The sweet potato has more fibre and a lower GI than potatoes and is therefore more suitable for those with **diabetes**.

Nutrients per serving
Sweet potato
GI low (54) • Fat 1 g • Carbohydrate 21 g • Fibre 3 g • Protein 2 g • kJ 480
ONE SERVING IS EQUIVALENT TO 1 1/2 STARCH AND MINIMAL FAT
GL 12

Nutrients per serving
Baby potatoes
GI intermediate (62) • Fat 1 g • Carbohydrate 19 g Fibre 2 g • Protein 2 g • kJ 497
ONE SERVING IS EQUIVALENT TO 1 1/2 STARCH AND MINIMAL FAT
GL 14

Spaghetti and bean bolognaise

Serves 4

150 g uncooked durum wheat spaghetti
5 ml (1 t) canola or olive oil
2 rashers lean bacon, chopped (optional)
2 medium onions, peeled and chopped
5 ml (1 t) crushed garlic or 2 cloves garlic
1 carrot, peeled and grated coarsely
1 green pepper, seeded and chopped
4 tomatoes, peeled and diced
10 ml (2 t) dried thyme
10 ml (2 t) dried origanum
10 ml (2 t) dried basil
2 ml (1/2 t) salt
freshly ground black pepper to taste
1 x 410 g tin brown beans, drained
1/2 x 410 g tin white beans, drained
1 x 65 g or 70 g tin tomato paste
20 ml (4 t) Parmesan cheese

1. Cook the spaghetti in lightly salted water until done.
2. Heat the oil in a large saucepan, and gently fry the bacon, onion, garlic, carrot, and green pepper until the onion is transparent. If it sticks add 15–30 ml (1–2 T) water and stir.
3. Add the diced tomatoes and simmer for 5 minutes
4. Add herbs, salt, pepper, beans and tomato paste and simmer for a further 5 minutes
5. Lightly mix the cooked spaghetti into the bean and tomato mixture, if desired.
6. Spoon onto a serving dish and sprinkle with Parmesan cheese.
7. Serve immediately with either two cooked vegetables or a tossed salad.

Dieticians' notes

- This meal is ideal for **carbo-loading** as it contains plenty of long-acting carbohydrates with not too much fat and protein.
- For a vegetarian version, omit the bacon.

Nutrients per serving

GI low (34) • Fat 5 g • Carbohydrate 55 g • Fibre 13 g • Protein 17 g • kJ 1 490

ONE SERVING IS EQUIVALENT TO 2 STARCH, 2 PROTEIN AND 2 VEGETABLES
GL 19

Fettuccine with mushrooms

Serves 4

5 ml (1 t) canola or olive oil
125 g (1/2 packet) lean bacon, visible fat removed and thinly sliced (optional)
150 g (3 c) uncooked fettuccine pasta
100 g small mushrooms, sliced or 1 x 200 g tin mushrooms, drained
2 ml (1/2 t) crushed garlic
5 ml (1 t) wholegrain mustard
30 ml (2 T) red or white wine, optional
15 ml (1 T) cornflour
30 ml (2 T) water
250 ml (1 c) low-fat milk
freshly ground black pepper
30 g (1 matchbox) lower fat Cheddar cheese, grated
10 ml (2 t) Parmesan cheese

Nutrients per serving

GI low (35) • Fat 10 g • Carbohydrate 33 g • Fibre 2 g • Protein 18 g • kJ 1 221

ONE SERVING IS EQUIVALENT TO 2 STARCH AND 2 PROTEIN
GL 11

1. Heat the oil in a non-stick saucepan and cook the bacon until browned.
2. Meanwhile, in a large saucepan of boiling water with 1 ml (1/4 t) salt, boil the fettuccine, uncovered, until just tender. Drain.
3. Add the mushrooms and garlic to the bacon and cook for 2 minutes, or until the mushrooms are cooked.
4. Stir in the mustard and wine and cook a further 3 minutes.
5. Mix the cornflour and water to a smooth paste, add to the sauce and stir over low heat until the mixture becomes a thick paste. Remove from the heat and gradually add the milk and pepper, stirring until well combined. Return to heat and cook until the sauce is thick and creamy.
6. Pour the sauce over the pasta, sprinkle with grated cheeses and serve immediately with a salad to complete the meal.

Dieticians' notes

- Cornflour has a very high GI and we usually try to leave it out or use oat bran instead. In this dish there are so many other low GI ingredients, and so little cornflour is used, that it is quite safe.
- For a vegetarian version, omit the bacon, and double the mushrooms.
- This is a tasty low-fat version of the usual pasta dish with the creamy sauce you get in restaurants

Bobotie

Serves 6

5 ml (1 t) oil
2 onions, peeled and finely chopped
2 cloves garlic, crushed, or 5 ml (1 t) dried crushed garlic or flakes
500 g topside mince
22 ml (1½ T) curry powder – may seem a lot, but the lentils suck up all the flavour
2 ml (½ t) salt
30 ml (2 T) 'lite' or ordinary chutney
15 ml (1 T) smooth apricot jam
15 ml (1 T) Worcestershire sauce
5 ml (1 t) turmeric
30 ml (2 T) brown vinegar
60 ml (¼ c) oat bran
1 x 410 g tin brown lentils or 250 ml (1 c) cooked lentils
100 ml (2/5 c) sultanas
2 eggs
250 ml (1 c) low-fat milk
pinch each salt and turmeric

Nutrients per serving (with rice)
GI low (39) • Fat 11 g • Carbohydrate 26 g • Fibre 5 g • Protein 28 g • kJ 1 708

ONE SERVING IS EQUIVALENT TO 1 STARCH, 3 PROTEIN AND 1 FRUIT/VEGETABLE
GL 10

1. Preheat the oven to 180 °C.
2. Heat the oil in a saucepan and fry the onion and garlic until soft. Add the meat and fry until brown.
3. Add the curry powder, salt, chutney, apricot jam, Worcestershire sauce, turmeric and vinegar to the meat and onion mixture. Mix well.
4. Add the oat bran, lentils and sultanas to the meat and simmer for a few minutes. Remove from the heat.
5. Add one egg, mix well and spoon into a greased ovenproof dish. Level the mixture.
6. Beat the other egg with the milk, salt and turmeric.
7. Pour egg and milk over the meat, put bay leaves on top and bake in the preheated oven for 1 hour.
8. Serve with 125–250 ml (½–1 c) cooked brown or basmati rice per person and a large salad.

Dieticians' notes

- As soon as red meat is used, the fat content goes up. But this is such a lovely high-fibre, lower fat version of a traditional South African dish, that we felt we had to include it.
- Because the lentils are well disguised in this dish, it is an ideal way to introduce reluctant legume eaters to this nutritious food.
- Although apricot jam has an intermediate GI, the lentils in the dish cancel out its effect. So, if you have **diabetes**, add the jam for that extra flavour and be assured of good blood glucose control.

Tasty pork casserole

Serves 10

6 rashers salt-reduced lean bacon, cut into strips, all visible fat removed
2 onions, peeled and sliced
1 pkt mushroom soup powder
3 ml (½ t) white pepper
800 g pork fillet, diced
1 x 410 g tin white beans, drained
250 ml (1 c) white wine or water
250 ml (1 c) water
250 g (1 punnet) mushrooms, sliced (optional)

Nutrients per serving (with 100 g pasta)
GI low (41) • Fat 9 g • Carbohydrate 36 g • Fibre 4 g • Protein 27 g • kJ 1 578

ONE SERVING IS EQUIVALENT TO 3 PROTEIN AND 2 STARCH
GL 15

1. 'Fry' the bacon and onion in a little water until the onion is transparent and the bacon is crisp.
2. Mix a third of the soup powder and pepper and roll the pork pieces in the mixture. Add the pork pieces and beans to the onion and bacon. Heat and mix well.
3. Mix the rest of the mushroom soup powder with the white wine and water and pour the mixture over the beans and pork. Add the mushrooms. Turn the heat down and simmer for 40 minutes, until the pork is done.
4. Serve on 125 ml (½ c) pasta or basmati rice, and with vegetables.

Dieticians' notes

- No salt is needed in this recipe because of the soup powder.
- The only reason we can use the high GI soup powder is because of the beans in the dish, which help to keep the GI down.

Roast lamb and beans

Serves 8

This is a very easy meal to prepare as it literally cooks itself. All the vegetables are roasted with the meat and only the gravy needs thickening just before serving.

1 leg of lamb, deboned (± 1 kg)
10 ml (2 t) ground cumin
4 cloves of garlic cut into slivers, or
 10 ml (2 t) crushed garlic or 10 ml (2 t) garlic flakes
500 ml (2 c) peach juice
1 ml (1/4 t) salt
freshly ground pepper to taste
3 small sweet potatoes
3 carrots, sliced
6 baby marrows, sliced
4 onions, quartered
1 x 410 g tin white beans, drained
60 ml (1/4 c) plain, low-fat yoghurt
15 ml (1 T) gravy powder or cornflour
parsley for garnishing

1. Preheat the oven to 160 °C.
2. Trim off as much of the outer layer of fat on the roast as possible. Rub the cumin into the meat.
3. Make little nicks in the surface of the meat and tuck in the garlic slivers.
4. Put the lamb into a large roasting pan with a lid or cover with aluminum foil.
5. Add the peach juice to the roast, season lightly with salt and pepper. Cover and roast for 1 hour, baste continuously.
6. Add sweet potatoes, carrots, baby marrows and onions and roast, covered, for another 30 minutes, basting occasionally.
7. Add the beans to the vegetables in the roasting pan. Cover and roast for 30–40 minutes.
8. To serve, remove the beans from the roasting pan and spread in a thick layer on a large platter. Arrange the vegetables on top of the beans.
9. Place the roast under the grill for about 5 minutes to brown, if necessary. Slice the meat and layer it on top of the vegetables.
10. Heat the cooking juices from the meat in a saucepan. Mix the yoghurt with the gravy powder and add to the sauce. Season to taste. Stir and cook until the sauce thickens.
11. Pour some sauce over the meat, beans and vegetables. Garnish with lots of parsley.
12. Serve with a mixed salad to complete the meal.

An unusual, yet delicious, Sunday roast.
Roasting the beans in the meat gravy gives them a lovely rich flavour. Even the most ardent legume hater will have to admit that this way beans are quite accepable.

Dieticians' notes

- As soon as red meat is used, the fat content is always higher. For this reason the meat portion is kept very small. This recipe, with only 8 g of fat per person, is a real bonus.
- Leg of lamb has the lowest fat content of all lamb cuts.
- We usually do not advocate the use of gravy powder or cornflour, but in this case the low GI beans and yoghurt compensate for the high GI cornflour or gravy powder.
- This meal is exceptionally high in fibre.

Nutrients per serving

GI low (46) • Fat 8 g • Carbohydrate 34 g • Fibre 6 g • Protein 32 g • kJ 1506

ONE SERVING IS EQUIVALENT TO 3 PROTEIN, 1 1/2 STARCH AND VEGETABLE
BUT REMEMBER THIS IS A WHOLE MEAL.
GL 16

Macaroni mince dish

Serves 4

150 g (1 1/2 c) durum macaroni, uncooked
5 ml (1 t) canola or olive oil
1 onion, peeled and chopped
1 clove garlic, crushed
1 x 65 g tin tomato paste
200 g topside minced beef
3 ml (1/2 t) mixed dry herbs
30 ml (2 T) chopped parsley
60 ml (1/4 c) uncooked split lentils
200 ml (4/5 c) stock (1/2 stock cube and 200 ml water)
15 ml (1 T) Worcestershire sauce
1 ml (1/4 t) salt
freshly ground black pepper to taste
5 ml (1 t) 'lite' margarine
30 ml (2 T) cake flour
2 ml (1/2 t) each mustard and nutmeg
100 ml (2/5 c) cooking water from vegetables
100 ml (2/5 c) skim/fat-free milk
extra tomato slices for garnishing
60 g (2 matchboxes) lower fat Cheddar cheese

1. Cook the macaroni in plenty of lightly salted water. Set aside.
2. Heat the oil and fry the onion for 1–2 minutes. Add the garlic and then the tomato paste and meat. Stir well and add the herbs, chopped parsley and split lentils.
3. Moisten the mixture with 200 ml stock. Add the Worcestershire sauce and season to taste. Simmer for 30 minutes.
4. For the white sauce, melt the margarine. Whisk in the flour, mustard, nutmeg, stock and milk, whisking all the time. Bring to the boil and simmer, stirring until the mixture thickens.
5. Remove from heat and mix the sauce with the cooked macaroni.
6. Place half the macaroni mixture in an ovenproof dish. Spoon the meat over. Cover with the remainder of the macaroni and then the tomato slices. Sprinkle the grated cheese on top.
7. Bake for 30 minutes in a preheated oven at 180 °C.

Dieticians' notes

- Despite the fact that this recipe contains so little minced meat, it just makes the 10 g fat per portion aimed at. Using any red meat immediately increases the fat content considerably.
- Be sure to use **lean** topside mince, skim milk and lower fat cheese.

Nutrients per serving
GI low (34) • Fat 10 g • Carbohydrate 41 g • Fibre 5 g • Protein 25 g • kJ 1 488

ONE SERVING IS EQUIVALENT TO 2 STARCH AND 3 PROTEIN
GL 14

Meat pie

Serves 6

5 ml (1 t) canola or olive oil
1 medium onion, peeled and chopped
400 g topside mince
1x 410 g tin baked beans in tomato sauce
4 tomatoes, peeled and chopped
5–25 ml (1–5 t) chilli powder
1 ml (1/4 t) salt
freshly ground black pepper to taste
PIE TOPPING
1/2 x 410 g tin white beans, drained
100 ml (2/5 c) low-fat milk
60 ml (1/4 c) water
1 egg
250 ml (1 c) cake flour, sifted before measuring
10 ml (2 t) baking powder
pinch of salt

1. Heat the oil and fry the onion until soft, add the meat and fry until brown. Add the beans, tomatoes and chilli. Season to taste.
2. Simmer for 10–15 minutes. Add water if necessary.
3. For the topping, mash the beans together with the milk, water and egg, or process in a food processor or liquidiser.
4. Sieve the flour, baking powder and salt onto the beans. Mix well. Spoon the meat mixture into an ovenproof dish. Spread the topping over the meat.
5. Bake for 20–25 minutes in a preheated oven at 220 °C.
6. Serve hot with cooked vegetables or a large salad.

Dieticians' notes

- An unusual dish with a low fat and very high fibre content.
- Beans are legumes and contain both starch and protein. They can therefore be regarded as either starch, or protein, or half-starch and half-protein.

Nutrients per serving
GI low 51 • Fat 9 g • Carbohydrate 37 g • Fibre 9 g • Protein 23 g • kJ 1 383

ONE SERVING IS EQUIVALENT TO 2 STARCH AND 3 PROTEIN OR 3 STARCH AND 2 PROTEIN
(see *Dieticians' notes*)
GL 19

Moussaka with soufflé topping

Serves 6

2 large brinjals, sliced (or 3 medium)
5 ml (1 t) canola or olive oil
1 large onion, peeled and chopped
5 ml (1 t) crushed garlic
1/2 green pepper, seeded and chopped
250 g topside mince
250 g brown mushrooms, sliced (1 punnet)
3 large tomatoes, peeled and chopped
10 ml (2 t) brown sugar
2 ml (1/2 t) cinnamon
2 ml (1/2 t) salt
100 ml (2/5 c) fresh parsley, chopped
1 x 410 g tin mixed beans, drained

TOPPING

5 ml (1 t) 'lite' margarine
45 ml (3 T) flour
125 ml (1/2 c) low-fat milk
250 ml (1 c) cooking water from vegetables
2 egg whites
salt and freshly ground black pepper to taste
2 ml (1/2 t) nutmeg
90 g (3 matchboxes) lower-fat Mozzarella cheese, grated

Nutrients per serving
(without pasta or rice)
GI low (35) • Fat 10 g • Carbohydrate 25 g • Fibre 10 g • Protein 20 g • kJ 1 238

ONE SERVING IS EQUIVALENT TO 1 STARCH AND 3 PROTEIN
GL 9

1. Place 30 ml (2 T) water at a time in a large frying pan and steam the brinjal slices until cooked, but not too soft. Remove the brinjals and set aside.
2. Add oil to the pan and gently fry the onion, garlic and green pepper until the onion is transparent.
3. Add the minced meat and fry until browned.
4. Add the mushrooms and when soft, add the tomatoes, sugar, cinnamon, salt, parsley and beans. Cover and simmer for about 20 minutes.
5. For the topping, melt the margarine and stir in the flour, milk and half the vegetable stock with a whisk. Cook, stirring continuously, until thick and smooth. Add more vegetable stock if too thick.
6. Whisk the egg whites until stiff, and fold with the seasoning into the white sauce.
7. Alternate layers of brinjal slices and bean-mince mixture in an ovenproof dish, beginning and ending with a layer of brinjal.
8. Pour the topping over and sprinkle with the grated cheese.
9. Bake for 30 minutes at 180 °C. Turn off the oven and allow to stand in the oven for 15 minutes before serving.

Serve with a large salad and basmati rice or durum wheat pasta, if desired, but remember to add one portion of starch per person for every 125 ml (1/2 c) cooked rice or pasta added.

Dieticians' notes

- For a vegetarian version, the minced meat may be left out altogether and another tin of beans used in its place.
- This moussaka is a very easy and tasty way to introduce legumes. The beans are part of the minced meat sauce and so are well disguised. Legumes have to be a *part* of the meal, and not *the* meal for those who are not used to them.
- Always use durum wheat pasta as it has a low GI. Home-made pasta made with flour has a high GI.
- **Slimmers** should skip the rice or pasta, as the beans in this dish already supply the starch. Add a large salad, or more vegetables instead.

Mini meatballs

Makes 24 small meatballs or 6 hamburger patties

125 ml (1/2 c) red split lentils (dry)
400 g minced topside beef
1 medium onion, peeled and finely chopped
1/2 small green pepper, seeded and finely chopped
5 ml (1 t) crushed garlic
10 ml (2 t) dried mixed herbs
60 ml (1/4 c) tomato sauce, or 'lite' tomato sauce
1 egg, lightly beaten
2 ml (1/2 t) salt
freshly ground black pepper
180 ml (3/4 c) oat bran or lower GI oats

Nutrients per mini meatball
GI low (37) • Fat 2 g • Carbohydrate 4 g • Fibre 1 g • Protein 5 g • kJ 251

1 MINI MEATBALL IS EQUIVALENT TO 1 PROTEIN
4 MINI MEATBALLS ARE EQUIVALENT TO 3 PROTEIN
GL8

1 HAMBURGER IS EQUIVALENT TO 3 STARCH AND 3 PROTEIN
GL 27

1. Cook the lentils in a saucepan of boiling water for 20 minutes or until soft. Drain well.
2. Preheat the oven to 200 °C while preparing the mince mixture.
3. In a bowl, combine the lentils, beef, onion, green pepper, garlic, herbs, tomato sauce, egg, salt and pepper. Mix well. Add enough oat bran for a burger consistency. Shape into 24 small meatballs and place on a lightly greased baking tray.
4. Bake for about 40 minutes, or until cooked, turning halfway through the cooking time. Serve hot with 2–3 cooked vegetables or a large salad, and mustard or chutney if desired.

These meatballs make a great picnic snack if served cold, dipped into a sauce made of chutney and low-fat cottage cheese, or a dip made of 'lite' mayonnaise and chutney in a 1:1 ratio (remember to count 1 fat).

Dieticians' notes

- If making **hamburgers**, ordinary bread rolls can be used as these patties have a very low GI. Together the roll and the patty would have a GI of 57, but the amount of starch is a little high with a GL of 27 per hamburger

Liesbet's curried mince

Serves 6
Quick and easy for when you are in a hurry!

5 ml (1 t) canola or olive oil
1 onion, peeled and chopped
1/4 green pepper, seeded and chopped
500 g topside mince
1 large brinjal, diced
2 ml (1/2 t) crushed garlic
5 ml (1 t) dried mixed herbs
2 ml (1/2 t) paprika
15 ml (1 T) vinegar
30 ml (2 T) red wine (optional)
15 ml (1 T) Worcestershire sauce
30 ml (2 T) tomato sauce, or 'lite' tomato sauce
30 ml (2 T) braai sauce or BBQ sauce
5 ml (1 t) stock powder (1/4 cube)
5 ml (1 t) curry powder
5 ml (1 t) turmeric
5 ml (1 t) masala
250 ml (1 c) raw basmati rice, or 500 ml (2 c) pasta, or 250 ml (1 c) pearl barley

1. Heat the oil and gently fry the onion and green pepper until the onion is transparent. Add the meat, breaking it up while stirring and fry gently. Add the diced brinjal and fry lightly.
2. Add remaining ingredients, except rice, and mix well. Simmer on low heat until meat is done. Add water if necessary.
3. Cook the rice, pasta or pearl barley in lightly salted water.
4. Serve the curried mince on the pasta, pearl barley or basmati rice with a large tossed salad, or with 2 cooked vegetables, or sambals such as chopped onion and tomato; cucumber in plain, low-fat yoghurt; and green banana.

This mild curry dish is also suitable for children.
For a stronger curry, use 10 ml (2 t) each of the curry powder and masala.

Dieticians' notes

- With pasta the GI drops to 40, with pearl barley it drops to 18!
- Barley is high in soluble fibre, which actively binds cholesterol and also helps with blood glucose control.

Nutrients per serving (with basmati rice)
GI low (50) • Fat 8 g • Carbohydrate 22 g • Fibre 2 g • Protein 20 g • kJ 1 071

ONE SERVING WITH STARCH IS EQUIVALENT TO 1 STARCH, 2 PROTEIN AND VEGETABLE
GL 11

Herbed lamb and pasta

Serves 4

150 g (1 3/4 c) durum wheat pasta tubes, e.g. penne, ziti
5 ml (1 t) canola or olive oil
250 g deboned lamb, any cut, all visible fat removed, cut into 1 cm cubes
1 onion, peeled and chopped
1 stalk celery, chopped
10 ml (2 t) crushed garlic
5 ml (1 t) dried tarragon
5 ml (1 t) dried rosemary, crumbled
1/2 chicken stock cube dissolved in
250 ml (1 c) boiling water
1 x 410 g tin baked beans in tomato sauce
60 ml (1/4 c) chopped parsley

1. In a large pot of lightly salted boiling water, cook the pasta until just tender. Drain well.
2. Meanwhile, in a large non-stick frying pan, heat the oil over medium heat until hot but not smoking. Add the lamb and cook, stirring frequently, for 3 minutes until no longer pink.
3. Add the onion, celery, garlic, tarragon and rosemary, and cook for another 3 minutes, stirring gently.
4. Add the stock and beans and bring to the boil. Simmer for about 5 minutes, stirring frequently and mashing some of the beans against the side of the pan, until the sauce is slightly thickened.
5. Add the parsley, toss with the hot pasta and serve with a large salad.

The mashed beans in this sauce add heartiness and thicken the sauce. The parsley adds a bright green colour.

Dieticians' notes

- Mutton and lamb are the fattiest red meats available. It is for this reason that so little is used in this recipe, together with beans help to bring the fat content of the dish down.
- This dish is suitable for **carbo-loading** as it is high in slow-release carbohydrates, and low enough in fat and protein.
- Pasta made from durum wheat (semolina) has a low GI. Home-made pasta made from flour has a high GI, as does commercial pasta made from soft wheat.
- Remember, that even though pasta has a low GI, it is a very concentrated carbohydrate source and thus portions must be kept small, as has been done in this recipe.

Nutrients per serving

GI low (40) • Fat 7 g • Carbohydrate 47 g • Fibre 10 g • Protein 24 g • kJ 1 440

One serving is equivalent to 2 starch, 3 protein and vegetable

GL 19

Pasta Alfredo

Serves 4

150 g flat ribbon noodles (1/3 of 500 g packet)
5 ml (1 t) canola or olive oil
100 g smoked ham, finely slivered
10 ml (2 t) chicken stock powder (1/2 stock cube) dissolved in 180 ml (3/4 c) boiling water
750 ml (3 c) broccoli, chopped
60 ml (1/4 c) fresh basil leaves, chopped
freshly ground black pepper
200–250 g fat-free cottage cheese (1 tub)
60 ml (4 T) fat-reduced cream
15 ml (1 T) flour
250 ml (1 c) cherry tomatoes, quartered

1. Cook pasta in lightly salted water until just tender. Drain well.
2. In a large non-stick frying pan, heat the oil over medium heat until hot, but not smoking. Add the ham and cook for about 2 minutes, stirring occasionally, until lightly crisped.
3. Add the stock, broccoli, basil and pepper and bring to boil. Reduce the heat and simmer until the broccoli is cooked.
4. In a food processor, combine the cottage cheese, cream, and flour and process for 1 minute only, to a smooth purée. Add the cheese mixture to the pan, stirring until well combined.
5. Add the tomatoes and cook until the sauce has thickened and the tomatoes are heated through.
6. Toss the sauce with the hot pasta, divide among 4 plates and serve with a salad.

Black forest ham, which is cured and smoked, has an intense flavour and texture and gives the best results. It is sold at most deli counters.

Nutrients per serving

GI low (33) • Fat 7 g • Carbohydrate 34 g • Fibre 4 g • Protein 20 g • kJ 1 163

ONE SERVING IS EQUIVALENT TO 2 STARCH, 2 PROTEIN/DAIRY AND VEGETABLE
GL 11

Dieticians' notes

- It is important to use fat-free cottage cheese and fat-reduced cream to keep the fat content low.
- This dish is suitable for **carbo-loading**, especially if double the pasta is used. The total carbohydrate per portion would then be 60 g carbohydrate.

Pasta with vegetable ragout

Serves 4

150 g (1 3/4 c) shell noodles
5 ml (1 t) canola or olive oil
250 g (1 packet) lean bacon, all visible fat removed, diced
2 celery stalks, thinly sliced
2 carrots, thinly sliced
10 ml (2 t) crushed garlic
500 ml (2 c) cabbage, cut into 1 cm chunks
1/2 bunch spinach, chopped finely
1 x 410 g tin tomatoes, chopped
5 ml (1 t) dried origanum and marjoram
60 g (2 matchboxes) Mozzarella cheese, grated

1. Cook the pasta in a large saucepan of lightly salted water until just tender. Drain well.
2. Meanwhile, in a large non-stick frying pan, heat the oil over medium heat until hot, but not smoking. Add the bacon and cook, stirring frequently, until lightly crisped.
3. Add celery, carrots, and garlic and cook, stirring frequently, until the vegetables are cooked.
4. Add the cabbage and spinach and cook, stirring all the time until the cabbage is wilted.
5. Add the tomatoes with the juice, add the herbs, and cook, stirring until all the flavours are blended, for about 5 minutes.
6. Toss the sauce with the hot pasta, divide among four plates, sprinkle with the cheese and serve.

Nutrients per serving

GI low (35) • Fat 10 g • Carbohydrate 38 g • Fibre 7 g • Protein 18 g • kJ 1 312

ONE SERVING IS EQUIVALENT TO 2 STARCH, 2 PROTEIN AND VEGETABLES
GL 13

Dieticians' notes

- This dish is suitable for **carbo-loading** with extra pasta.

Pasta with mince and mushrooms

Serves 4

150 g (1 1/2 c) durum wheat pasta tubes, e.g. penne or macaroni
5 ml (1 t) canola or olive oil
1 onion, peeled and finely chopped
1 celery stick, chopped
125 g mushrooms, coarsely chopped (1/2 punnet)
10 ml (2 t) crushed garlic
300 g topside mince
60 ml (1/4 c) wine
10 ml beef stock powder (1/2 stock cube) dissolved in 125 ml (1/2 c) boiling water
1/2 x 410 g tin tomatoes, chopped, with their juices
10 ml (2 t) sugar, optional
freshly ground black pepper to taste

Nutrients per serving

GI low (37) • Fat 9 g • Carbohydrate 34 g • Fibre 3 g • Protein 21 g • kJ 1 282

ONE SERVING IS EQUIVALENT TO 2 STARCH, 2 1/2 PROTEIN AND VEGETABLE
GL 12

1. Cook pasta in lightly salted water until just tender. Drain well.
2. Meanwhile, heat the oil in a large non-stick frying pan. Add the onion, celery, mushrooms and garlic and cook for about 10 minutes, stirring frequently, until the vegetables are soft.
3. Add the minced meat and cook until no longer pink. Add the wine, increase the heat and cook until almost evaporated.
4. Add the stock, tomatoes, sugar and pepper, cover and simmer for about 15 minutes until the sauce is rich and flavourful.
5. Divide the pasta among 4 bowls, spoon the sauce over, and serve.

This sauce freezes well. Freeze it in 4 individual portions and thaw in the microwave as needed.

Dieticians' notes

- As soon as red meat is used, the fat content of the meal automatically increases. Note that extra lean or topside mince must be used, and that very little is used.
- This meal is suitable for **carbo-loading,** especially if the pasta is doubled.

Vegetable and beef stir-fry

Serves 6

250 g spaghetti, broken into 3–4 cm pieces
5 ml (1 t) canola or olive oil
1 medium onion, peeled and chopped
15 ml (1 T) grated fresh or 5ml (1 t) dried ginger
1 clove garlic, crushed (5 ml [1 t] minced garlic)
200 g minute steaks, cut into thin strips
1 stalk celery, sliced
1/2 small yellow pepper, seeded and chopped
1/2 medium red pepper, seeded and chopped
200 g (2 c) cauliflower florets
1 large carrot, cut into matchsticks
200 g (2 c) broccoli, chopped
250 g mushrooms, sliced (1 punnet)
1 x 410 g tin asparagus salad cuts, drained, water reserved
15 ml (1 T) soya sauce
20 ml (4 t) cornflour
200 ml (4/5 c) water

1. Cook the spaghetti in a large saucepan of lightly salted water until just tender. Drain and keep warm.
2. Heat the oil in a wok or large non-stick frying pan. Add the onion, ginger, garlic and steak. Stir-fry over medium heat for about 3–5 minutes or until the steak is almost cooked. Add the remaining vegetables and stir-fry until just tender, sprinkling in a little water if necessary.
3. Mix the soya sauce, cornflour and the water from the tinned asparagus until smooth. Add the cornflour mixture to the stir-fry and stir until the mixture boils and thickens. Add the water as required if the sauce gets too thick. Add the spaghetti and stir until heated through. Serve immediately.

Dieticians' notes

- Suitable for **carbo-loading**, especially if the spaghetti is doubled. (Carbohydrates are then pushed up to 68 g per portion).
- Asparagus is not recommended for those suffering from gout. Simply leave it out.
- Use soya sauce sparingly, as it is very high in sodium.

Nutrients per serving

GI low (37) • Fat 4 g • Carbohydrate 39 g • Fibre 6 g • Protein 18 g • kJ 1 088

ONE SERVING IS EQUIVALENT TO 1 1/2 STARCH, 2 PROTEIN AND 2 VEGETABLES
GL 14

Yoghurt fruit jelly

Serves 8

1 x 410 g tin fruit cocktail in natural juice
1 x 85 g packet raspberry-flavoured jelly powder (sugar free optional)
500 ml (2 c) low-fat flavoured or plain yoghurt

Nutrients per serving

GI low (50) • Fat 1 g • Carbohydrate 24 g • Fibre 1 g • Protein 4 g • kJ 481

ONE SERVING IS EQUIVALENT TO 1 STARCH, 1/2 DAIRY/PROTEIN AND 1/2 FRUIT
GL 12

1. Drain the fruit cocktail and measure the juice. Add enough water to make 250 ml (1 c) of liquid.
2. Bring the juice and water to the boil and then pour it over the jelly powder in a bowl. Stir until dissolved and cool, but do not allow to set.
3. When the jelly just begins to set, fold the yoghurt and fruit through the jelly and mix well.
4. Pour the mixture into 8 serving bowls, cover and refrigerate until set.

Dieticians' notes

- In this case, normal jelly can safely be used as we know that sugar has an intermediate GI, and with the yoghurt the GI is lowered even further.
- **Slimmers** should rather use plain fat-free yoghurt to reduce the 'starch' (sugar). Remember to omit the starch at the meal you are eating this with.

Baked pear and pasta pudding

Serves 8

125 g (1 c) durum wheat spaghetti, broken into 1 cm lengths
375 ml (1 1/2 c) low-fat milk
150 ml (3/5 c) soft brown sugar
10 ml (2 t) 'lite' margarine
15 ml (1 T) grated lemon rind
30 ml (2 T) ground almonds
2 eggs, separated
6 tinned pear halves in natural juice, drained

Nutrients per serving

GI low (46) • Fat 5 g • Carbohydrate 28 g • Fibre 2 g • Protein 6 g • kJ 729

ONE SERVING IS EQUIVALENT TO 2 STARCH AND 1 PROTEIN
GL 13

1. Preheat the oven to 190 °C.
2. Cook the spaghetti in plenty of lightly salted boiling water for 10 minutes, until just soft. Drain and place in a saucepan with the milk. Simmer for 5 minutes.
3. Remove the pan from the heat and let it cool.
4. Add the sugar and stir to dissolve. Add the margarine, lemon rind, ground almonds and beaten egg yolks.
5. Whisk the egg whites until stiff peaks form and fold into the pasta mixture. Pour this mixture into a greased ovenproof dish. Arrange the pear halves on top.
6. Bake in the preheated oven for 30 minutes.

For a really different and delicious pudding, try this one. Once you get over the idea that pasta should not be in a sweet dish, you will love it.

Dieticians' notes

- This is a good **carbo-loading** pudding. Low in fat, yet high in low GI carbohydrates, and not too much protein.
- Please note that this pudding contains 2 starches. Use half the pasta and only 125 ml (1/2 c) sugar to lower the carbohydrates to 1 starch per serving.
- Remember to compensate for the starch in this dessert by having no starch with your meal.

Low-fat custard

Makes 4 x 125 ml (1/2 c) servings or 8 x 60 ml servings (1/4 c)

500 ml (2 c) low-fat milk or skim milk
30 ml (2 T) sugar
30 ml (2 T) custard powder
5 ml (1 t) vanilla essence (optional)

1. Bring 400 ml (1 3/5 c) of the milk to the boil.
2. While the milk is heating up, place the remaining 100 ml (2/5 c) of the milk and the sugar in a small bowl and mix to dissolve the sugar. Add the custard powder and stir to a smooth paste.
3. Just as the milk begins to bubble, pour half of it onto the custard powder mixture and stir. Pour this back into the hot milk and bring to the boil, stirring. Cook until thickened.
4. Add 5 ml (1 t) vanilla essence, if desired.
5. Serve cold with any one of the low GI puddings.

To make banana custard, use half a banana per person with 125 ml (1/2 c) custard. The GI then rises by one point to 53. Remember to count 1 fruit extra.

Dieticians' notes

- In the GI tables used in Australia, the GI of custard is given as 43. In South Africa we have not yet tested the GI of custard. The value we have given is the calculated value, based on the ingredients in this recipe.
- We feel quite sure that the true, tested GI of custard will be lower than the calculated value, due to the interaction of the nutrients with each other, especially when eaten cold.
- When custard is hot, it has a higher GI value than when it is eaten cold. This is due to a change in the crystal structure of the cooked starch when it cools down. The starch in this case is the custard powder.
- People with **diabetes,** please note that if eaten cold, this low-fat custard is quite safe and will not suddenly raise your blood glucose levels. It has a low GI despite the sugar in it!
- **Slimmers**, do not forget to omit one starch at the meal if you are having custard for pudding.

Nutrients per serving

GI low (52) • Fat 2 g • Carbohydrate 15 g • Fibre negl. • Protein 4 g • kJ 417

ONE 125 ML (1/2 C) PORTION IS EQUIVALENT TO 1 STARCH AND 1/2 DAIRY
GL 8

ONE 60 ML (1/4 C) PORTION IS EQUIVALENT TO 1 STARCH
GL 4

Apple crumble

Serves 8

1 x 410 g tin pie apples
10 ml (2 t) lemon juice
30 ml (2 T) raw honey, warmed
60 ml (1/4 c) flour
250 ml (1 c) oat bran or lower GI oats
60 ml (1/4 c) 'lite' margarine
60 ml (1/4 c) soft brown sugar
1 ml (1/4 t) salt

1. Place the pie apples in a greased pie dish, and pour the lemon juice and honey over.
2. Rub together the flour, oats, margarine, brown sugar and salt and sprinkle this mixture over the apples.
3. Bake in the oven at 180 °C until the crust is brown.
4. Serve with fat-reduced cream or custard made with low-fat milk, if desired (see recipe above).

Dieticians' notes

- The nutritional analysis is for the crumble on its own, without the low-fat custard or fat-reduced cream.
- A good dessert for **carbo-loading**; high in carbohydrates and low enough in protein and fat.
- **Slimmers** should only eat half a portion and then omit the starch from the meal eaten with it.

Nutrients per serving

GI intermediate (56) • Fat 5 g • Carbohydrate 24 g • Fibre 2 g • Protein 2 g • kJ 619

ONE SERVING IS EQUIVALENT TO 1 STARCH, 1/2 FRUIT AND 1 FAT
GL 14

Cherry delight

Serves 12

A delicious pudding for that special dinner party

- 1 x 410 g tin white beans, drained
- 1/2 packet (72.5 g) Boudoir biscuits
- 60 ml (1/4 c) sherry (optional)
- 200–250 g (1 tub) low-fat or fat-free cottage cheese
- 250 ml (1 c) plain, low-fat yoghurt
- 10 ml (2 t) vanilla essence
- 1 packet vanilla instant pudding
- 1 x 410 g tin cherries in syrup
- 10 ml (2 t) gelatine

1. Mash the beans or process in a food processor until smooth, but not for longer than 3 minutes.
2. Arrange the biscuits in a single layer in an attractive glass serving dish and sprinkle the sherry over them.
3. Beat the beans, cottage cheese, yoghurt, vanilla essence and instant pudding together with an electric beater or hand whisk.
4. Spread the mixture evenly over the biscuits and refrigerate until set.
5. Drain the cherries and cut in half. Arrange on top of the set cottage cheese filling.
6. Mix the gelatine into the cherry syrup and stir the mixture over low heat, until all the gelatine has dissolved. Cool.
7. When it is cool to the touch, pour the cooled cherry juice mixture over the pudding and refrigerate until set.

Nutrients per serving

GI low (52) • Fat 2 g • Carbohydrate 25 g • Fibre 2 g • Protein 7 g • kJ 652

One serving is equivalent to 1 starch and 1 dairy/protein
GL 13

Dieticians' notes

- This recipe contains high GI ingredients such as the Boudoir biscuits, the syrup from the cherries and the instant pudding powder. However, the beans, cottage cheese and the yoghurt offset these, and the end result is a low GI pudding.
- This makes it a good choice of pudding for people with diabetes and hypoglycaemia, despite the sugar in it!
- **Slimmers** should remember to leave out one starch and have less protein at the meal where this pudding is eaten.

Baked warm pudding

Serves 12

- 1 x 410 g tin white beans, drained
- 2 eggs
- 75 ml (5 T) low-fat milk
- 10 ml (2 t) caramel essence
- 30 ml (2 T) 'lite' margarine
- 100 ml (2/5 c) brown sugar
- 180 ml (3/4 c) self-raising flour
- 10 ml (2 t) baking powder
- 1 ml (1/4 t) ground cloves
- 1 ml (1/4 t) ground cinnamon
- 180 ml (3/4 c) oat bran
- 15 ml (1 T) vinegar
- 60 ml (1/4 c) sultanas
- 2 ml (1/2 t) salt

1. Preheat the oven to 180 °C.
2. Mash the drained beans with the eggs, milk and essence, or process in a food processor, but not for longer than 2 minutes.
3. Cream the margarine and sugar and add the bean mixture. Mix well.
4. Sieve the flour, baking powder and spices together. Add the oat bran and lift a few times with the spoon to incorporate air.
5. Add the flour mixture to the bean mixture and stir well. Add the vinegar, sultanas and salt.
6. Spoon into a greased pan (20 x 20 cm) and bake at 180 °C for 35–40 minutes.
7. Serve hot with cold low-fat custard (page 106).

Nutrients per serving (without custard)

GI intermediate (58) • Fat 3 g • Carbohydrate 21 g • Fibre 3 g • Protein 5 g • kJ 587

One serving is equivalent to 1 1/2 starch and 1 fat
GL 12

Dieticians' notes

- A double portion of this pudding with 125 ml (1/2 c) custard would make a good **carbo-loading** pudding – 58 g carbohydrates per portion, with very little fat and not too much protein.
- **Slimmers** should omit the starch at the meal where this pudding and custard is served.

Fruit salad

Serves 6

1 small papino, peeled and seeded
1 small green apple
1 small red apple
3 oranges
1 banana
1 kiwi fruit
10 large grapes
10 ml (2 t) sugar (optional)
30 ml (2 T) lemon juice, or grenadilla pulp

1. Cut the papino into cubes. Cut the apples into quarters (do not peel), remove the core and then chop into cubes.
2. Using a sharp knife, peel the oranges as you would an apple. Slide the blade of the knife between the segments and push the whole, peeled segments out into a bowl.
3. Peel and slice the banana.
4. Peel the kiwi fruit, cut in half lengthwise and slice thickly.
5. Cut each grape in half and remove the seeds.
6. Mix all the fruit together, add the lemon juice or grenadilla pulp and sugar, if desired, and mix thoroughly. Chill before serving.

Nutrients per serving

GI low (46) • Fat 0 g • Carbohydrate 23 g • Fibre 4 g • Protein 1 g • kJ 439

ONE SERVING IS EQUIVALENT TO 1½ FRUIT
GL 11

Dieticians' notes

- Adding lemon juice or grenadilla pulp lowers the GI of the fruit salad.
- With the sugar, the GI of the whole fruit salad is 47. The reason for this is that the fruit has a lower GI than the sugar, so the sugar, with the higher GI, slightly increases the GI. But even at 47 the GI is quite acceptable.
- **Tropical fruits** have higher GI values, and **decidious** and **citrus fruits** have lower GI values. The more tart (sour) a fruit, the lower its GI.

Apricot or peach cheesecake

Serves 12

This is a really impressive dessert and very more-ish!

½ packet (100 g) digestive biscuits
200–250 g (1 tub) low-fat cottage cheese
80 ml (⅓ c) sugar
175 ml (1 small tub) or 180 ml (¾ c) low-fat apricot yoghurt
2 eggs, separated
15 ml (1 T) gelatine
60 ml (¼ c) cold water
5 ml (1 t) vanilla essence
pinch of salt
2 x 410 g tins apricots or peaches in natural juice
20 ml (4 t) gelatine

1. Arrange the biscuits in a single layer in a 26 cm pie dish.
2. Using an electric beater, whisk the cottage cheese, sugar, yoghurt and egg yolks until smooth.
3. Soften 15 ml (1 T) gelatine in the cold water and dissolve slowly over low heat. Slowly beat gelatine into cottage cheese mixture. Add vanilla.
4. Whisk egg whites stiffly with the pinch of salt and then fold into the cottage cheese mixture. (Be sure to use clean beaters!)
5. Pour onto the biscuits and refrigerate for 2 hours until firm.
6. When the cheesecake is set, drain the fruit, reserving the juice in a saucepan (for the stove) or a glass jug (for the microwave). Heat the fruit juice and 20 ml (4 t) gelatine until the gelatine is completely dissolved. Leave until cool to the touch.
7. Meanwhile, arrange the fruit on top of the cheesecake filling.
8. Spoon the cooled juice evenly over the fruit until all the fruit is just covered. Discard any excess juice and gelatine.
9. Return to the refrigerator until firm enough to slice.

Nutrients per serving

GI intermediate (59) • Fat 9 g • Carbohydrate 16 g • Fibre 1 g • Protein 7 g • kJ 696

ONE SERVING IS EQUIVALENT TO ½ STARCH, ½ FRUIT AND ½ DAIRY
GL 9

Dieticians' notes

- Normally cheesecake is made with cream and high-fat pastry, which makes for a very high-fat dessert.
- This recipe is as delicious as normal cheesecake, yet contains less than one-third of the normal fat content. The bonus is that it also has a lower GI and GL.
- **Slimmers** should remember to have 1 starch less at the meal eaten with this cheesecake.

Carrot cake

Cuts into 16 slices

200 ml (180 g) 'lite' margarine
180 ml (3/4 c) sugar
250 ml (1 c) cake flour, sifted before measuring
pinch of salt
5 ml (1 t) bicarbonate of soda
7 ml (1 1/2 t) ground cinnamon
2 ml (1/2 t) ground nutmeg
pinch of ground cloves
10 ml (2 t) baking powder
250 ml (1 c) oat bran
3 eggs
125 ml (1/2 c) grated carrot (1 large or 2 small carrots)
3 grated apples
150 ml (3/5 c) sultanas

ICING
200–250 g (1 tub) low-fat cottage cheese
45 ml (3 T) icing sugar
5 ml (1 t) vanilla essence

1. Cream margarine and sugar for not more than 3 minutes.
2. In a separate bowl, sift the flour, salt, bicarbonate, spices and baking powder together. Add the oat bran, lifting the mixture with a spoon to incorporate air.
3. To the margarine and sugar, add eggs one by one, adding 30–45 ml (2–3 T) dry ingredients with each egg. Beat no more than 1 minute after each addition.
4. Stir the rest of the dry ingredients into the egg mixture using a wooden spoon. Fold in the raw carrots, apple and sultanas.
5. Place in a greased 25 cm ring pan and bake at 160 °C for 30–45 minutes. Leave to cool completely and remove from pan.
6. Mix ingredients for the icing. Spread over the top of the cake.
7. Cut into 16 thin slices when serving.

Dieticians' notes

One slice of carrot cake with icing is a meal on its own. **Slimmers** need to compensate by omitting the starch and a fat at their next meal.

Nutrients per slice

GI intermediate (63) • Fat 8 g • Carbohydrate 26 g • Fibre 2 g • Protein 5 g • kJ 809

ONE SERVING WITH ICING IS EQUIVALENT TO 1 1/2 STARCH, 1 FRUIT AND 2 FAT
GL 16

Boston loaf

Cuts into 16 slices

125 ml (1/2 c) rooibos tea
250 ml (1 c) dried fruit cake mix
250 ml (1 c) lower GI oats
1 x 410 g tin small white beans
2 eggs, beaten
150 ml (3/5 c) sugar
250 ml (1 c) flour, sifted
10 ml (2 t) baking powder
1 ml (1/4 t) salt
5 ml (1 t) lemon essence

1. Pour the hot rooibos tea over the dried fruit cake mix. Add the oats, stir well and leave to soak for 10 minutes.
2. Meanwhile, process the drained beans with one of the eggs in a food processor or liquidiser until smooth, but not for longer than 1–2 minutes.
3. Add the sugar and the other egg and process for 1 minute until combined.
4. Sift the flour and baking powder onto the fruit mixture and pour the bean mixture on top of this and then mix gently with a wooden spoon.
5. Add the salt and lemon essence and stir until combined.
6. Pour the mixture into a greased loaf pan and bake at 180 °C for 10 minutes. Reduce heat to 150 °C, bake for 1 hour until pale brown and cooked through.
7. Cut into 16 slices when serving.

This makes a tasty, dense and heavy teabread. Serve lightly spread with 'lite' margarine or eat as is.
If wrapped in tin foil, this cake will keep for 2 weeks. Perfect for taking on self-catering holidays.
Cakes made with beans need long, slow baking at a low temperature.

Nutrients per slice

GI intermediate (60) • Fat 1 g • Carbohydrate 27 g • Fibre 3 g • Protein 4 g • kJ 589

ONE SLICE IS EQUIVALENT TO 2 STARCH
GL 16

Dieticians' notes

- This teabread is suitable for **carbo-loading** as it is low in fat, and high in lower GI carbohydrates and not too high in protein. It should preferably be eaten as is, without any margarine.
- **Slimmers** remember that 1 slice contains 2 starch. Only have a thin slice and leave out the starch at your next meal.

Orange and sultana loaf

Serves 16

1 unblemished orange, scrubbed clean
1 x 410 g tin white beans, drained
200 ml (4/5 c) sugar
20 ml (4 t) canola or olive oil
2 eggs, beaten
150 ml (3/5 c) sultanas
5 ml (1 t) bicarbonate of soda
200 ml (4/5 c) self-raising flour
60 ml (4 T) oat bran
150 ml (3/5 c) Hi-Fibre Bran cereal
1 ml (1/4 t) salt
5 ml (1 t) vanilla essence

ICING

60 ml (4 level T) icing sugar
10 ml (2 t) lemon juice

1. Preheat the oven to 180 °C.
2. Cut the unpeeled orange into quarters and remove any pips or blemishes. Place the orange quarters, skin and all, into a liquidiser or food processor and process for 30 seconds. Scrape down the sides and process for another 60 seconds until the orange is chopped up into small pieces.
3. Add the drained beans and process for another 30 seconds. Add the sugar.
4. Pour the orange mixture into a large mixing bowl and add the oil and eggs. Stir with a wooden spoon until well mixed.
5. Add the sultanas and mix.
6. Sift the bicarbonate and flour over the orange mixture, add the oat bran and the Hi-Fibre Bran cereal, and mix well with a wooden spoon. Add the salt and vanilla and stir well.
7. Spoon into a greased bread tin. Bake at 180 °C for 15 minutes. Turn the oven down to 150 °C, cover the top of the cake with foil, and bake for another 90 minutes. Cool completely.
8. For the icing, mix the icing sugar with the lemon juice, and drizzle over the top of the cooled cake.
9. Cut into 16 thin slices when serving.

Nutrients per slice

GI intermediate (59) • Fat 2 g • Carbohydrate 28 g • Fibre 3 g • Protein 4 g • kJ 618

ONE SLICE IS EQUIVALENT TO 1 1/2 STARCH, 1 FRUIT AND 1/2 FAT

GL 16

This seems like a really odd mixture at first, but it makes the most delicious cake – crisp on the outside and moist on the inside.

Dieticians' notes

- A good **carbo-loading** cake. High in slowly absorbed carbohydrates, low in fat and protein.
- **Slimmers** note that if you eat a slice of this, you need to omit your starch at the next meal.

Apricot tart

Serves 10

375 ml (1 1/2 c) lower GI oats
1 large apple, grated
75 ml (5 T) flour
2 ml (1/2 t) salt
125 ml (1/2 c) sugar
60 ml (1/4 c) 'lite' margarine, melted
60 ml (1/4 c) low-fat milk
1 egg, beaten
1 x 410 g tin apricots in natural juice, drained
10 ml (2 t) brown sugar

Nutrients per slice

GI low (55) • Fat 5 g • Carbohydrate 27 g • Fibre 2 g • Protein 3 g • kJ 703

ONE SLICE IS EQUIVALENT TO 1 1/2 STARCH, 1/2 FRUIT AND 1 FAT

GL 15

1. Mix the oats, apple, flour, salt, sugar, then add the margarine, milk and egg.
2. Gently mix to a slightly sloppy batter.
3. Grease a pie dish, spoon in half the mixture and press down firmly.
4. Place apricots on top of the batter and then spoon the rest of the mixture on top of the apricots. Smooth over with a knife.
5. Sprinkle with 10 ml (2 t) brown sugar.
6. Bake for 25–30 minutes at 200 °C until the top is brown and crisp. Allow to cool.
7. Cut into 10 small wedges or squares and serve with tea or coffee.

These are crispy topped wedges of tasty soft 'biscuit', made in the shape of a pie and cut up into small wedges. This tart is best eaten fresh.

Dieticians' notes

- This is a delicious tea-time treat, but because oats are used instead of flour it is rather heavier than one would expect.
- **Slimmers** take note that you need to omit the starch and a fat in your meal, if you have this for pudding.

Health rusks

Makes 60 rusks

250 ml (1 c) oat bran or lower GI oats
500 ml (2 c) cake flour, sifted
25 ml (5 t) baking powder
500 ml (2 c) digestive bran
500 ml (2 c) Hi-Fibre Bran cereal
500 ml (2 c) whole-wheat ProNutro
5 ml (1 t) salt
250 ml (1 c) sultanas
2 apples, peeled and grated
250 ml (1 c) 'lite' margarine or 100 ml (2/5 c) oil
250 ml (1 c) sugar
1 egg
500 ml (2 c) low-fat fruit yoghurt, any flavour (pear or vanilla works well)
5 ml (1 t) vanilla essence
5 ml (1 t) bicarbonate of soda

1. In a large bowl, mix the first 7 ingredients. Add the sultanas and the grated apple and with a wooden spoon lift up the mixture a few times to incorporate air.
2. Melt the margarine and sugar. Remove from heat.
3. Beat egg and stir in yoghurt and vanilla essence. Add to melted margarine (or oil) and sugar mixture. Add the bicarbonate of soda to the liquid mixture and stir to blend. Leave to bubble 1–2 minutes.
4. Pour the liquid ingredients onto the dry ingredients and mix until just blended. Add low-fat milk if too stiff. The dough should not be sloppy, but soft enough to spoon into pans.
5. Spoon into two sprayed bread pans and bake for 30 minutes at 180 °C. Turn down the heat to 150 °C and bake for 45 minutes.
6. Cut into 30 fingers per loaf and dry the rusks in a slow oven at 100 °C for 2–3 hours.

These are rather more-ish rusks despite their being so healthy.
This recipe can successfully be halved, should one wish to make a smaller batch of rusks.

Nutrients per rusk

GI low (54) • Fat 2 g • Carbohydrate 13 g • Fibre 3 g • Protein 2 g • kJ 356

One serving is equivalent to 1 starch
GL 7

Dieticians' notes

- These rusks make a good **carbo-loading** snack.
- If raisins are used instead of sultanas, the GI is raised to 56, as the GI of raisins is higher than that of sultanas.
- The rusks will not be as sweet if only plain, low-fat yoghurt is used, and the GI and GL a little lower.

Apricot biscuits

Makes 40 bars or biscuits

150 ml (3/5 c) 'lite' margarine
200 ml (4/5 c) soft brown sugar
1 egg
5 ml (1 t) vanilla essence
500 ml (2 c) flour, sifted before measuring
5 ml (1 t) baking powder
250 ml (1 c) lower GI oats
pinch of salt
5 ml (1 t) cinnamon
150 ml (3/5 c) apricot spread

1. Cream the margarine and sugar until light and fluffy, but not for more than 2–3 minutes.
2. Add the egg and vanilla essence and beat for 1 minute.
3. Sift the flour and baking powder and add to the mixture. Mix.
4. Add the oats, salt and cinnamon, and work to a soft, crumbly dough; add skim or low-fat milk, if necessary.
5. Press and pat half the mixture into a greased 30 cm x 20 cm swiss roll pan.
6. Spread evenly with apricot spread and grate the remainder of the dough on top.
7. Bake at 180 °C for 25–35 minutes.
8. When cool, cut into 40 bars, fingers or biscuits.

Nutrients per biscuit

GI intermediate (62) • Fat 2 g • Carbohydrate 12 g • Fibre 0.5 g • Protein 1 g • kJ 299

One biscuit is equivalent to 1 starch
GL 7

Dieticians' notes

- Remember that beating a batter too long or vigorously can increase the GI.
- If diabetic (sugar-free) apricot spread is not available, ordinary apricot jam may be used.
- Omitting the jam or spread altogether **raises** the GI to 66!

Apple and spice biscuits

Makes 30 biscuits

250 ml (1 c) oat bran
125 ml ($^1/_2$ c) flour
125 ml ($^1/_2$ c) whole-wheat ProNutro
5 ml (1 t) baking powder
125 ml ($^1/_2$ c) Hi-Fibre Bran cereal
125 ml ($^1/_2$ c) sugar
1 apple, finely grated
2 ml ($^1/_2$ t) ground cinnamon
1 ml ($^1/_4$ t) ground cloves
60 ml ($^1/_4$ c) 'lite' margarine
1 egg, beaten

Nutrients per biscuit

GI intermediate (59) • Fat 1.5 g • Carbohydrate 8 g
Fibre 1 g • Protein 1 g • kJ 220

ONE BISCUIT IS EQUIVALENT TO $^1/_2$ STARCH
GL 5

1. Mix all the dry ingredients with the grated apple and spices.
2. Rub the margarine into the mixed dry ingredients.
3. Stir in the egg, and mix to a stiff dough.
4. Using a teaspoon in each hand, place a heaped teaspoon of batter at a time on a lightly greased baking sheet and flatten to a round biscuit, or flatten onto a baking tray and cut into squares.
5. Bake at 180 °C for about 15 minutes or until lightly browned.
6. Carefully lift each biscuit off the baking sheet onto a cooling rack using an egg lifter. The biscuits are very soft as they come out of the oven, but become crisp on the outside as they cool.

This recipe makes for satisfyingly soft, chewy biscuits because of the apple in the dough.

Dieticians' note

- These biscuits are particularly low in fat. Traditionally, biscuits have a high fat content, so this is a real bonus.

Orange and lemon biscuits

Makes 30 biscuits

125 ml ($^1/_2$ c) flour
10 ml (2 t) baking powder
2 ml ($^1/_2$ t) ground nutmeg
125 ml ($^1/_2$ c) whole-wheat ProNutro
375 ml (1$^1/_2$ c) lower GI oats, firmly packed
100 ml ($^2/_5$ c) 'lite' margarine
125 ml ($^1/_2$ c) sugar
1 ml ($^1/_4$ t) salt
1 egg
15 ml (1 T) grated orange rind (rind of 1 orange)
45–60 ml (3–4 T) lemon juice (juice of 1 lemon)

Nutrients per biscuit

GI intermediate (60) • Fat 2 g •
Carbohydrate 9 g • Fibre 1 g • Protein 1 g • kJ 259

ONE BISCUIT IS EQUIVALENT TO $^1/_2$ STARCH AND $^1/_2$ FAT
GL 5

1. Sift flour, baking powder and nutmeg together; then add Pronutro and oats. Set aside.
2. Cream margarine, sugar and salt, add the egg and orange rind, and stir well.
3. Add the dry ingredients alternately with the lemon juice, and mix well. If too dry, add a little more lemon juice.
4. Drop teaspoonfuls onto a greased baking sheet.
5. Bake at 190 °C for 15–20 minutes, until the biscuits start to brown.

These tangy biscuits are almost like rock cakes – quick and easy to make.

Dieticians' note

- Taking all the sugar out does not give the biscuits a lower GI since it is the concentrated cake flour that contributes the most to the higher GI value. However, removing the sugar will lower the carbohydrate per biscuit and thus lower the GL (to 3).

Recommended food/product list

Lower Glycemic Index and lower fat South African foods and products

High-fibre cereals
Bokomo Fibre Plus
Bokomo Bran Flakes
Bokomo Morning Harvest Muesli
Fine Form Muesli
Kellogg's Hi-Fibre Bran
Pick 'n Pay Shredded Bran
Kellogg's Fruitful All Bran
ProNutro, whole-wheat, apple bake
ProNutro, whole-wheat, original

Lower GI oats
Bokomo oats
Woolworths oats
Pick 'n Pay oats
Spar oats
Rolled oats
Jungle oat bran

Lower GI pasta (durum wheat)
Fattis & Monis spaghetti and macaroni
Fattis & Monis pasta shapes
Fine Form lasagne sheets and tagliatelle
Imported pastas
Woolworths dry pastas
Pick 'n Pay Choice pastas
Spar imported pastas

Lower GI rice
Old Mill Stream brown rice
Tastic white rice
Tastic basmati rice
Veetee's basmati rice
Pick 'n Pay Choice basmati rice

Wheat rice / pearled wheat
Lion Stampkoring / wheat rice
Crossbow Stampkoring / pearled wheat

Lentils
Lion brown lentils
Crossbow whole lentils
Imbo whole lentils
Imbo split lentils
Lion split lentils
Crossbow split lentils
Tiger 4-in-1 soup mix

Barley
Lion pearl barley
Crossbow pearl barley
Imbo pearl barley
Tiger pearl barley

Dry beans and peas, raw and canned
All brands of dry beans, and all varieties
Crossbow
Lion
Imbo
Mayfair
Rhodes
Gold Crest
Lesmel
Gibson
Hyperama
Pick 'n Pay Choice brand
Pick 'n Pay No Name brand
Sunkist
Marina
Farmgirl
Gold Dish
Koo
All Gold
Four in one soup mix, Tiger
Split Peas, Tiger

Lower GI breads
Astoria rye breads, wheat free
Fine Form seed loaf
Nature's Harvest brown seed loaf
Duens seed loaf
Olde Cape brown seed loaf
Woolworths seed loaf
Woolworths rye breads, wheat free
Pita pockets (Anat, Pick 'n Pay)

Lower GI crackers
Provita, original
Provita, multigrain
Jepsa's low GI rusks
Ouma Nutri rusks

Dairy products
Low-fat/fat-free fruit or plain yoghurt
Clover Danone
Dairybelle
Parmalat
Gero
Pick 'n Pay Choice
Woolworths
Spar

Low-fat/fat-free flavoured milks
Parmalat Yum Chums

Buttermilk
Bonnita, low fat (Parmalat)
Dairybelle, low fat

Cheeses
Lichten Blanc (Clover) (12% fat)
Dairybelle In Shape lower fat Cheddar (23%fat)
Elite Edam (24.5%fat)
Woolworths lower fat Cheddar (22% fat)
Woolworths lower fat Gouda (22% fat)
Mozzarella
Simonsberg Mozzarella (25.6% fat)

Low-fat cottage cheeses
(NB. Check labels for fat content)
Dairybelle
Lancewood
Parmalat
In Shape
Clover

Feta cheeses
Pick 'n Pay Choice Danish Style (14% fat)
Simonsberg 33%reduced fat (18.7% fat)
Pick'n Pay Traditional (22% fat)
Clover Traditional (28.5% fat)
Simonsberg (29% fat)
Dairybelle Original (33% fat)

Ice cream
Dialite
Country Fresh Lite range

Milks
Low-fat milk (2% fat)
Skim/fat-free milk (1% fat)
Nestlé Ideal Low Fat Evaporated milk

Leaner protein choices

Ostrich
Klein Karoo ostrich meats
Woolworths ostrich meats

Bacon
Like-It-Lean bacon
Back bacon, fat trimmed off
Shoulder bacon, fat trimmed off

Minced meat
Extra lean mince
Topside lean mince
Chicken mince
Veal mince

Tuna in brine
Pick 'n Pay
John West
Gold Crest

Pilchards
Lucky Star
Glenryck
Pick 'n Pay

Soya mince mixes
Imana
Vitamince
VegieMince

Lower fat mayonnaise/salad creams
Nola Lite reduced oil dressing (7.6% fat)
Trim low-oil dressing (10.5% fat)
Weigh-Less low-oil dressing (10% fat)
Nola Slim-a-naise (12% fat)
Figure (12% fat)
Pick 'n Pay low-oil salad cream (15% fat)
Kraft Miracle Whip Light (18% fat)
Crosse & Blackwell mayonnaise light (26% fat)
Hellmann's Light (31% fat)
Kraft Real Mayonnaise Light (34.6% fat)
Woolworths reduced oil dressing (12.2% fat)

Condiments
All Gold tomato sauce

Fruit juices

Ceres:
Apple
Cranberry and Kiwi
Secrets of the Valley
Mysteries of the Mountain
Whispers of Summer

Liqui-Fruit:
Apple
Apricot
Breakfast Punch
Mango-orange
Passion Power
Peach-orange
Tangerine Teaser

Jam
Naturlite jams
Fine Form apricot jam
Fine Form Seville orange marmalade
Rhodes fruit spreads

Tinned fruit
Naturlite, all variants

Oils
Olive oil, cold pressed
Canola oil, Epic
Canola oil, B-Well
Macadamia oil
Red Palm oil (Carotino)
Avocado oil
Peanut oil
Canolive oil (with basil)

Margarine
Flora light (50% fat)
Flora Extra light (35% fat)
Flora Liquid (78% fat)
Canola Lite (Blossom) (52% fat)

Lower fat coconut milk
Sunkist 'lite' coconut milk
Taste of Thai 'lite' coconut milk
GoldCrest 'lite' coconut milk

See the ***South African Glycemic Index and Load Guide*** for more detailed information on the GI of various foods eaten in South Africa – (available from most bookstores, your local dietitian, pharmacy or www.gabisteenkamp.co.za or www.gifoundation.co.za

For a list of dietitians in SA who use the GI in the treatment of patients, visit the GI Foundation SA website. www.gifoundation.co.za

For a general list of private practising dietitians in SA, visit the website of the Dietetics Association of SA www.dietetics.co.za

Index of recipes